The Complete Peanuts

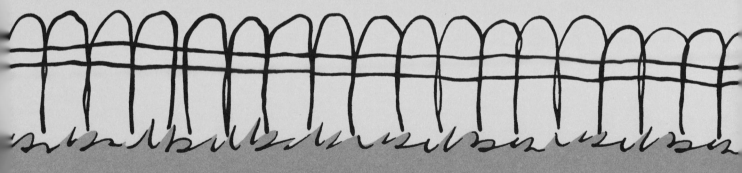

THE COMPLETE PEANUTS
by Charles M. Schulz

Editor: Gary Groth
Designer: Seth
Production Manager: Kim Thompson
Production, assembly, and restoration: Paul Baresh
Archival assistance: Marcie Lee
Index compiled by Kristen Bisson, Tom Graham, Ben Horak,
Janice Lee, and Anna Pederson
Associate Publisher: Eric Reynolds
Publishers: Gary Groth & Kim Thompson

Special thanks to Jeannie Schulz, without whom
this project would not have come to fruition.
Thanks also to John R. Troy and the
Charles M. Schulz Creative Associates,
especially Paige Braddock and Kim Towner.

First published in America in 2013 by Fantagraphics Books,
7563 Lake City Way, Seattle, WA, 98115, USA.

First published in Great Britain in 2015 by Canongate Books,
14 High Street, Edinburgh, EH1 1TE

1

British Library Cataloguing-in-Publication Data
A catalogue record for this book is available on request from the British Library.

ISBN: 978 1 78211 517 5
Printed and bound in China
www.canongate.tv

CHARLES M. SCHULZ

THE COMPLETE PEANUTS

1989 TO 1990

" THE FRIENDSHIP OF A BOY
AND HIS DOG IS A
BEAUTIFUL THING.."

CANONGATE BOOKS

Charles M. Schulz in 1985 during the filming of *It's Your 20th Television Anniversary, Charlie Brown*. Courtesy of The Charles M. Schulz Museum and Research Center, Santa Rosa, California.

FOREWORD by LEMONY SNICKET

Sometimes, a simple sentence in the morning paper is enough to send me back to bed. I've lost track of the number of days when I rise from slumber, pour my morning beverage and toast whatever I can find in the kitchen, and then sit in a chair and read something like this—

Everyone in the world is lonely. [198]

or this—

I've never seen anybody so completely useless. [312]

or this—

You wake up in the middle of the night, and everything seems hopeless...you're all alone. You wonder what life is all about, and why you're here and does anyone really care, and you just stare into the dark, and you feel all alone... [178]

or maybe just—

Help me, I'm lost. [43]

—whereupon I weep or moan or burn my toast or experience some other morning catastrophe. Where do I see such statements, you ask? In what section of the newspaper can one find such bitter and sad proclamations? Foreign Affairs? Opinion? Business?

Oddly enough, these frantic sentences are found in the section marked "Comics," from an inked serial melodrama that ran for half a century until the death of its author and illustrator, Charles M. Schulz, lowered the guillotine on the proceedings. The melodrama now runs again, over and over, in newspapers all over the world, like a spiral staircase forever taking you lower and lower. Over the years, this drama has been collected and released in volumes, presumably for readers who would rather have a great deal of pain at once rather than having it fed to them, spoonful by spoonful, over years of breakfasts. This book contains the sections of this melodrama which originally appeared in newspapers during the years 1989 and 1990, when things were miserable enough. Now this misery is yours.

The hero of this melodrama is a balding grammar school student paralyzed by fear and self-loathing. "I'd like to buy a box of valentine candy for a girl who doesn't know I exist," he says, adding "I'll never have the nerve to give it to her anyway." [20] It's no wonder he admits "I've always been sort of a useless person" [132] who "can't even daydream good." [25]

Text for Today
Genesis 19:26

He's a classic candidate for a mental health professional, but sadly the psychiatrist he chooses is also a child, who not only offers him nothing but cruelty and scorn during their sessions, but inappropriately socializes with him outside of the office and acts as a taunting athletic coach during their time outdoors. One would be tempted to label her as the villain in this ongoing tale of terror, if she didn't share the same unhappy hopelessness as her helpless patient—

So I ask myself what could be more stupid than standing out here in right field in the rain? I keep asking myself the same question over...what could be more stupid? Then I ask myself again...In the meantime, I'm getting wet. [207]

Even the most worthless psychiatrist knows that family life can dictate one's mental turmoil, and the young "doctor"'s problems may well stem from her younger brother, who shuffles around town clutching raggedy bedclothes and trying to dissolve one of his own fingers in his mouth. It's no wonder the psychiatrist has fallen into a cycle of romantic obsession and violent argument with a temperamental musician modeling himself after a long-dead German composer famed for dying in agonizing pain. The younger brother, meanwhile, is the subject of romantic scrutiny by a flighty and dim-witted child — *yet another child!* — who is none other than the sister of our glum, bald hero, creating a lovelorn and familial entanglement unmatched since Hamlet's mother first winked at Uncle Claudius.

Our hero, in the meantime, is not free from obsessive complications: two women compete for his attention, all the while maintaining a tense "friendship" with one another despite the fact that one of them, out of stupidity or malice, mistakes the gender of the other. Call a young woman "sir" enough times and you can't be surprised that she spends her time with a boy who constantly wallows in a cloud of his own filth.

Even the neighborhood dog, who by all rights should remain clueless of the goings-on, is ravaged by the local madness. When not talking to a bird who utters nothing but apostrophes, he fantasizes that he is fighting in one of the world's most horrifying conflicts, one that claimed millions and millions in bloody casualties and pro-voked a sequel that still stands as a benchmark for the greatest catastrophe known to man. The dog prefers such a daydream to watching these children treat each other with indifferent barbarity.

Despite this tinderbox of tension and fear, this melodrama, unlike *Macbeth* or *Crime and Punishment* or *Little House on the Prairie*, does not descend into bloodshed. Mr. Schulz's sense of doom is far quieter and more sinister. Instead, these children wander the neighborhood doing little else but contemplating their melancholy lives. There are a few fragments of plot — in the chapters included here, a teacher finds romantic misery at a baseball game, a dog wanders the desert hallucinating — but for the most part this melodrama is played out in conversation. Frustrated by their senseless suffering, the characters offer suspicious advice:

Never marry a musician and never answer the door. [233]

—implausible torture—

This is hard to believe, but my toes are caught in my binder. [115]

—resigned pessimism—

Someday...someone will ask you why we climbed this mountain, and you can answer simply, because it was there. Yes, I suppose you could also admit we had nothing else to do. [128]

—and increasing hysteria—

The world is coming to an end (in my opinion). Fill the water bottles! Stand in the doorways! Turn off the valves! Call Gramma! Board up the windows! Break out the rations! Get the spare blankets! Put on your boots! [304]

—and despite the fact that, in fifty years, none of these children get any older, they forlornly face the certain truth that the future will only bring more of the same:

Getting upset is good for you. It prepares you for all the things that are going to happen to you later in life. [231]*...Before you know it, you're old and you haven't really done anything... maybe it's better to just let the years go by.* [118]

Why do I read this melodrama? Why do I immerse myself, morning after morning, volume after volume, in these sad goings-on? Despite the fact that the characters in this saga derive little comfort from literature — "Why would anyone want to say 'good night' to the moon?" [213] asks the lovesick sister — I agree with our droopy hero when he says "I guess we all read what seems to interest us the most, don't we?" [101]

PSYCHIATRIC HELP 5¢

THE DOCTOR IS PREOCCUPIED

We do. I am fascinated by this endless, ghastly tale of these poor youngsters. I sink into their troubles like quicksand. I absorb episode after episode and hunger for more. In a way, this melodrama reminds me of some kind of foodstuff — individual portions of suffering, encased in a brittle shell of grainy philosophy that I pry open, again and again, to devour the material inside. It does not surprise me that some people are allergic to these things, but I find them addictive. They mash up in my mind, like something I'd spread on toast. I keep consuming them, over and over, a sad snack, some legume of despair, some grim bean salted with woe that I cannot bring myself to name.

1989
TO
1990

SIR, I THOUGHT WE WERE GOING TO THE MOVIES..

IN A MINUTE, MARCIE..I'M WATCHING DONNA ADAMEK BOWL.. SHE'S MY HERO..

BESIDES, IT'S HARD TO GET OUT OF A BEANBAG WHEN YOU'RE HOLDING A BOWLING BALL..

1-9

LISTEN TO THIS..THERE'S GOING TO BE AN "UGLY DOG" CONTEST..

"UGLY DOG"?

I THINK I'VE ALREADY FOUND THE WINNER!

1-10

WHY DON'T YOU WRITE TO YOUR BROTHER SPIKE WHO LIVES IN THE DESERT?

ASK HIM IF HE WANTS TO BE IN THE "UGLY DOG" CONTEST..

I'VE NEVER THOUGHT OF SPIKE AS BEING UGLY...

PATHETIC, MAYBE..

1-11

PEANUTS
by Schulz

THAT'S NOT SKATING.. THAT'S SLIDING!

YOU DON'T HAVE ANY SKATES ON! YOU'RE JUST SLIDING ON YOUR FEET..THAT'S NOT SKATING!

SKATING IS WHEN YOU HAVE SKATES ON! YOU'RE NOT SKATING AT ALL! YOU'RE JUST SLIDING!

HOW COULD I HAVE BEEN SO STUPID?

I THOUGHT I WAS HAVING FUN..

SEE? IT'S A PHOTOGRAPH OF ALL THE PUPPIES..SNOOPY AND SPIKE ARE RIGHT THERE IN FRONT...

BUT WHO'S THAT IN THE BACK ROW?

OLAF! THAT'S OLAF!

HE'S THE ONE WE SHOULD INVITE TO THE "UGLY DOG" CONTEST!

"UGLY OLAF"! THAT'S WHAT THEY USED TO CALL HIM..

WE WANT YOU TO WRITE TO YOUR BROTHER OLAF, AND INVITE HIM TO THE "UGLY DOG" CONTEST

I HAVEN'T SEEN OLAF IN YEARS..MAYBE HE ISN'T UGLY ANYMORE..

IN OUR FAMILY, THE OLDER WE GET, THE CUTER WE GET!

HOW DO YOU INVITE YOUR OWN BROTHER TO AN "UGLY DOG" CONTEST? I DON'T EVEN KNOW HOW TO BEGIN THE LETTER..

Dear Ugly,

I HATE PLAYING HOCKEY ON WOODSTOCK'S HOME ICE..

1-30

AT OTHER RINKS THEY PLAY THE NATIONAL ANTHEM BEFORE THE GAME...

HERE WE HAVE TO DO THE "HOKEY POKEY"!

THAT WAS THE FIRST MOVEMENT OF THE SYMPHONY, SIR..NOW, THEY'RE PLAYING THE SLOW MOVEMENT..

JUST LIKE MY LIFE..I'M IN THE SLOW MOVEMENT..

1-31

WHAT IS WRONG WITH THE FAMOUS WORLD WAR I FLYING ACE? HE HAS A VERY PAINED EXPRESSION...

IS HE HAVING TROUBLE WITH OUR FRENCH LANGUAGE? IS HE HAVING DIFFICULTY WITH THE IMPERFECT SUBJUNCTIVE?

NO, HIS SCARF IS CAUGHT ON THE BACK OF HIS CHAIR..

SCHULZ 2-1

GRAMMA SAYS SHE'S FOUND A NEW LITTLE RESTAURANT THAT SHE REALLY LIKES..

2-6

THEY SERVE SMALL PORTIONS..

BUT THE PRINT ON THE MENUS IS LARGE

WE JUST GOT OUR TEST BACK..I HATE TO LOOK...

I HOPE I DIDN'T GET A D-MINUS..

THEY SAY A D-MINUS CAN IMPAIR THE FUNCTION OF YOUR IMMUNE SYSTEM AND DISRUPT THE CHEMICAL BALANCE OF YOUR BODY..

2-7

SORRY, BODY

"THOUSANDS OF PEOPLE PARADED HAPPILY THROUGH THE STREETS, BUT ECONOMISTS PREDICT THE CLEANUP WILL BE COSTLY"

"SKIES WERE SUNNY TODAY, BUT ECONOMISTS WARN THAT THIS COULD CAUSE AN INCREASE IN THE PRICE OF SUNGLASSES..."

"ALTHOUGH AUDIENCES ACROSS THE COUNTRY LOVE THE FILM, ECONOMISTS ARE SAYING IT WILL PROBABLY LOSE MONEY"

LUNCH

FOUR, THREE, TWO, ONE..

LUNCH TIME, MARCIE..

IS THAT ALL YOU'RE HAVING, SIR?.. JUST FRENCH FRIES?

SO WHAT DO YOU HAVE THAT'S SO GREAT?

I HAVE A VERY HEALTHY LUNCH.. A CHEESE SANDWICH WITH SPROUTS, SOME CARROT STICKS, AN APPLE AND SOME CRANBERRY JUICE...

2-12

YOUR LUNCH SOUNDS HEALTHY ALL RIGHT, MARCIE, BUT IT ISN'T PERSONALIZED..

PERSONALIZED?

EACH FRENCH FRY HAS MY INITIALS ON IT!

WHY COULDN'T I HAVE GIVEN HER THE BOX OF CANDY, AND SAID, "HERE, THIS IS FOR YOU..I LOVE YOU"?

WHY COULDN'T I HAVE DONE THAT?

BECAUSE YOU'RE YOU, CHARLIE BROWN

2-16

NOW, I HAVE ANOTHER QUESTION..WHY DID I ASK YOU?

2-17

A DOG SHOULD NEVER BE LEFT ALONE IN THE CAR..

LEAVE YOUR GRANDFATHER IN THE CAR, BUT NOT THE DOG!

RIGHT NOW, MY PITCHER'S MOUND IS COVERED WITH SNOW, BUT PRETTY SOON IT'LL BE SPRING, AND I'LL BE THROWING THAT FIRST PITCH...

POW!!

2-18

..THEN I'LL BE LOOKING FORWARD TO WINTER AGAIN..

February

"AND NOW IT'S TIME FOR OUR BIBLE QUIZ"

"AND THE FIRST TO CALL IN THE CORRECT ANSWER WILL RECEIVE FOUR TICKETS TO THE UPCOMING JONI JAMES CONCERT!"

"HERE IS THE QUESTION.. 'WHAT DID SAMUEL CALL THE NAME OF THE STONE THAT HE SET BETWEEN MIZPEH AND SHEN?'"

"EBENEZER!" FIRST BOOK OF SAMUEL, CHAPTER SEVEN, TWELFTH VERSE!

OH, SURE..HE'S THE CUTE ONE... SURE, I KNOW..

SURE, HE'S CUTE, TOO.. I MEAN, YOU KNOW, LIKE, SURE...

WELL, I MEAN, WHO ELSE? COME ON! I MEAN, SURE...

"THAT'S CORRECT, MA'AM! CONGRATULATIONS"

A CONTEST, HUH? YOU SHOULD HAVE CALLED IN..

IT'S GOING TO BE A HISTORY TEST, AND I NEED YOUR HELP

FORTUNATELY, I THINK IT'LL PROBABLY BE MYSTICAL CHOICE

3-6

MULTIPLE CHOICE

WHATEVER

3-7

I HATE IT WHEN MY CADDIE SAYS, "I THINK I'LL STAND WAY OVER HERE IN CASE YOU SHANK IT!"

PSYCHIATRIC HELP 5¢

I MEAN, HOW WOULD YOU LIKE TO GO THROUGH LIFE BEING CALLED 'PIGPEN'?

THE DOCTOR IS IN

3-8

HOW ABOUT YOUR FATHER? WHAT DO PEOPLE CALL HIM?

THE DOCTOR

'PIGPEN, SENIOR'!

THE DOCTOR IS IN

YES, MA'AM..OUR BASEBALL TEAM IS PLAYING ITS FIRST GAME OF THE SEASON RIGHT AFTER SCHOOL TODAY...

3-13

WHY DON'T YOU COME AND WATCH US?

SARCASM DOES NOT BECOME YOU, MA'AM

ONE FINGER WILL MEAN A FAST BALL AND TWO FINGERS A CURVE..

WHAT ABOUT THREE FINGERS?

3-14

THREE FINGERS WILL MEAN LET 'EM HIT IT, AND WE'LL ALL GO HOME..

I'D BE CRAZY TO ASK ABOUT FOUR FINGERS

WHO'S THAT OVER THERE SITTING IN THE CAR?

THAT'S OUR TEACHER.. I INVITED HER TO COME WATCH OUR GAME...

I NEVER THOUGHT SHE'D DO IT

MAYBE SHE'S LONELY AND HAS NOWHERE ELSE TO GO..

3-15

THAT SOUNDS LIKE MY WHOLE TEAM..

HOLD IT JUST LIKE THAT..THANK YOU...

I DON'T UNDERSTAND YOU..

3-19

WHY DO YOU KEEP TRYING TO FLY THESE KITES WHEN YOU ALWAYS GET THEM TANGLED AROUND A TREE?

IT ALWAYS HAPPENS..

SOMETIMES YOU DON'T EVEN GET OUT OF OUR YARD...

WOULDN'T IT BE FUNNY IF YOU DIDN'T EVEN MAKE IT OUT THE FRONT DOOR?

VERY FUNNY

YES, MA'AM, I SAW YOU AT OUR GAME LAST WEEK..AND I SAW YOU GET INTO THAT OTHER CAR AND LEAVE..

THAT FELLOW YOU LEFT WITH...DO WE KNOW ANYTHING ABOUT HIM?

3-20

SORRY, MA'AM..I SOUND LIKE YOUR FATHER OR SOMETHING, DON'T I?

I THINK OUR TEACHER IS IN LOVE..

I WAS AFRAID OF THAT...

I'VE ALWAYS HOPED THAT SHE'D WAIT UNTIL I GREW UP, AND THEN MARRY ME..

3-21

HOW WOULD YOU SUPPORT HER?

WE COULD LIVE OFF HER RETIREMENT PAY

HEY, MANAGER, I THOUGHT IT MIGHT INCREASE ATTENDANCE IF WE HAD A "MASKED MARVEL" ON OUR TEAM..

3-22

BONK!

I CAN SEE THE "MASKED," BUT WHAT ABOUT THE "MARVEL"?!

LOOK, DID YOU SEE THAT? OUR TEACHER WAS WAITING IN HER CAR, AND HER BOYFRIEND DIDN'T SHOW UP...

SEE? SHE'S DRIVING AWAY ALONE...

SHANE! COME BACK, SHANE!

HER NAME ISN'T "SHANE"!

3-23

I SUPPOSE IT'S NONE OF MY BUSINESS, MA'AM, BUT I HATE TO SEE YOU FEELING SO SAD..

3-24

MAYBE YOU'LL FIND ANOTHER BOYFRIEND TOMORROW, OR MAYBE EVEN THIS AFTERNOON

JOE OPTIMIST..

MY DAD SAID HIS FIRST OWNER USED TO EAT TOAST FOR BREAKFAST EVERY DAY

HE'D BITE OFF A FEW CHUNKS, AND THEN GIVE MY DAD A LITTLE BIT OF WHAT WAS LEFT

3-25

MY DAD SAID IT WAS ALWAYS HIS DREAM TO SOMEDAY HAVE HIS OWN WHOLE SLICE OF TOAST..

TOUCH THIS BLANKET, YOU STUPID BEAGLE, AND YOU'LL REGRET IT FOR YEARS...SO YOU'D BETTER BACK OFF!

I CAN'T BACK OFF.. I CAN ONLY GO FORWARD

I CAN GO FORWARD AND MAKE RIGHT TURNS..

AFTER I MAKE A RIGHT TURN, I GO FORWARD AGAIN..

4-9

NOW, ANOTHER RIGHT TURN..

HERE I AM GOING FORWARD AGAIN..

ANOTHER RIGHT TURN..

HELP ME..I'M LOST!

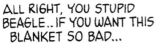

SORRY, MA'AM, I WAS ASLEEP.. AND I DREAMED I WAS SLEEPING, BUT IN THE DREAM WHERE I WAS SLEEPING, I DREAMED I WAS AWAKE...

5-1

THEN IN THE DREAM WHERE I WAS AWAKE, I FELL ASLEEP, AND IN THE DREAM WHERE I WAS SLEEPING I HEARD YOUR VOICE AND WOKE UP

ANYWAY, I THINK THAT'S HOW IT WAS.. DID YOU ASK ME A QUESTION?

PLEASE DON'T CRY, MA'AM..

SHOULD I, OR SHOULDN'T I?

I SHOULD

5-2

ONE HESITATES TO OFFEND A DOUGHNUT BY NOT EATING IT..

OKAY, TEAM, THIS IS AN IMPORTANT GAME..

LET'S ALL TRY TO PLAY OUR BEST...

I THOUGHT YOU SAID **LOOK** OUR BEST!

5-3

I HAVE TO WRITE A REPORT ON WHY WE'RE HERE..

5-4

WHO KNOWS?

GOOD..THAT WAS EASIER THAN I THOUGHT..

THE TEACHER SAID MY REPORT ON "WHY WE'RE HERE" WASN'T LONG ENOUGH..

How should I know, and who cares?

THAT'S A LOT LONGER..

AND IT HAS MORE DEPTH..

5-5

MY WATER DISH IS GONE!

WHY WOULD ANYONE WANT TO TAKE MY WATER DISH?

5-6

It

"IT"... YES, I LIKE THAT

It was a dark and stormy night.

"'YOU NEVER TAKE ME ANYPLACE,'SHE COMPLAINED"

"How can I take you anyplace when it's a dark and stormy night?" he said.

5-7

"THEIR MARRIAGE WAS RAPIDLY COMING APART"

They were behind with their car payments, and the rent on the condominium was due.

WHAT A SAD LITTLE STORY..

I'LL BE ANXIOUS TO SEE HOW YOU GET THEM OUT OF THEIR TROUBLES..

Suddenly, their dog, Rex, decided he'd better take over!

YOU LOOK KIND OF LONELY SITTING THERE

5-15

I GUESS MAYBE I AM..

THERE'S NOTHING MORE LONELY THAN SITTING ON A BENCH ALL BY YOURSELF WITHOUT A DOUGHNUT..

?

5-16

DO YOU MIND IF I TRY SITTING WAY BACK HERE, MA'AM?

I THINK MAYBE I CAN RETURN YOUR QUESTIONS BETTER FROM THE BASELINE..

THE EARS HEAR THE CAN OPENER..

RIGHT AWAY THE STOMACH KNOWS THAT SUPPER IS COMING..

HOW DO THE EARS TELL THE STOMACH?

I'VE NEVER BEEN ABLE TO FIGURE THAT OUT..

5-17

May

IF I FAIL THAT TEST TOMORROW, IT'LL BE YOUR FAULT, CHUCK, BECAUSE WE TALKED ON THE PHONE TOO MUCH..

YOU'RE THE ONE WHO KEEPS CALLING ME!

YOU SHOULDN'T ANSWER THE PHONE, CHUCK..

5-25

I KNEW IT, CHUCK! I FAILED THE TEST TODAY BECAUSE INSTEAD OF STUDYING, I WAS TALKING ON THE PHONE WITH YOU!

5/26

IT WAS YOUR FAULT CHUCK

MY FAULT ?!

DON'T BE TOO HARD ON YOURSELF, CHUCK..

IF A BALL COMES YOUR WAY, DON'T YELL, "I GOT IT!" UNLESS YOU'RE SURE YOU'VE GOT IT...

5-27

I GOT IT!

BONK!

THERE ARE SO MANY THINGS IN LIFE THAT WE CAN NEVER BE SURE ABOUT..

CAVEAT EMPTOR.." LET THE BUYER BEWARE"

I SUPPOSE THAT WAS ONE OF THE FIRST THINGS YOU LEARNED IN LAW SCHOOL...

5-29

NO, I LEARNED IT WHEN THE HANDLE FELL OFF THIS CHEAP BRIEFCASE!

YES, MA'AM..ONLY TWO MORE WEEKS OF SCHOOL...

BUT I PROMISE THAT I'M GOING TO BE STUDYING AS HARD AS I CAN..

THIS OFFER IS GOOD FOR A LIMITED TIME ONLY..

5-30

THERE'S AN ARTICLE HERE ABOUT A MAN WHO GOT FED UP WITH EVERYTHING..SO YOU KNOW WHAT HE'S GOING TO DO ?

5-31

HE'S DECIDED TO DEVOTE THE REST OF HIS LIFE TO MAKING HIS DOG HAPPY..

GET THAT MAN'S ADDRESS!

MARCIE AND CHUCK HAVE GONE OFF TO CAMP WHILE I HAVE TO STAY HOME AND GO TO SUMMER SCHOOL...I'M SO JEALOUS I CAN'T STAND IT!

6-8

WHY AM I SO DUMB IN SCHOOL? WHY CAN'T I GET BETTER GRADES?

SOMETIMES I THINK MAYBE I TORE ALL THE LIGAMENTS IN MY HEAD..

HI, MARCIE..SORRY TO BOTHER YOU AT CAMP, BUT I WAS JUST SORT OF WONDERING HOW YOU AND CHUCK ARE DOING..

DON'T STAND SO CLOSE, CHARLES, AND YOU'RE SQUEEZING MY HAND TOO HARD!

6-9

JUST TEASING YOU, SIR..

YES, MA'AM, I'M PART OF THE D-MINUS COMMUNITY...

WELL, I ADMIT I'D RATHER BE GOING TO CAMP INSTEAD OF SUMMER SCHOOL..

BUT YOU CAN BET YOUR LIFE I'M GONNA STUDY REAL HARD BECAUSE MAYBE I CAN STILL MAKE IT TO CAMP!

6-10

Z

"CONCERT ETIQUETTE... DO NOT OPEN CANDIES WRAPPED IN CELLOPHANE"

"TRYING TO BE QUIET BY OPENING WRAPPERS SLOWLY ONLY PROLONGS THE TORTURE OF THOSE AROUND YOU"

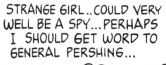

I KNOW I'M NOT SUPPOSED TO BE HERE, MARCIE, BUT I KEPT THINKING ABOUT YOU AND CHUCK UP HERE TOGETHER, AND IT WAS DRIVING ME CRAZY!

WHERE IS CHUCK? I WANT TO SEE HIM..

HE GOT LONELY FOR HIS DOG SO HE WENT HOME

6-19

I CAN'T STAND IT

SNOOPY, I'M HOME! I MISSED YOU SO MUCH I CAME HOME!

AREN'T YOU GLAD TO SEE ME?

6-20

DON'T THEY REALIZE HOW DANGEROUS IT IS TO ALLOW UNAUTHORIZED PERSONNEL ON THE RUNWAY?

I GOT MYSELF IN A LOT OF TROUBLE, CHUCK, AND IT WAS ALL YOUR FAULT!

MY FAULT?!

I SNEAKED AWAY FROM SCHOOL JUST TO SEE YOU, AND THEN I FOUND OUT YOU HAD GONE HOME TO BE WITH YOUR DOG..

6-21

MY FAULT?

I'M SURE SHE'S A SPY.. HANG UP ON HER!

I MISSED YOU WHEN I WAS AWAY AT CAMP.. DID ANYTHING EXCITING HAPPEN WHILE I WAS GONE?

THERE I WAS AT TWO THOUSAND FEET OVER ST. JUVIN..SUDDENLY A FOKKER TRIPLANE APPEARED ABOVE ME!

6-22

I JUST GOT BACK FROM CAMP MYSELF, CHARLES.. IT WASN'T MUCH FUN AFTER YOU LEFT...

WAS YOUR DOG GLAD TO SEE YOU WHEN YOU GOT HOME?

6-23

IF SHE'S FROM THE RED CROSS, ASK HER ABOUT THOSE MEDICAL SUPPLIES WE ORDERED..

WHEN YOU AND CHUCK WERE AT CAMP, MARCIE, DID YOU DO A LOT OF THINGS TOGETHER?

WELL, THERE WAS THE MOONLIGHT WALK..

MOONLIGHT WALK!?! AAUGH!!

6-24

IT WASN'T MUCH OF A WALK.. WE JUST GOT STARTED WHEN CHARLES WALKED INTO A TREE!

IF WE'RE GOING TO CROSS THIS STREAM, TROOPS, WE'LL HAVE TO BUILD A RAFT..

WOODSTOCK HAS THE AX SO HE'LL CHOP DOWN THE TREES..THE REST OF US WILL GATHER VINES...

BONK!

6-25

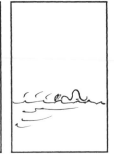

HOW DID YOU GET OVER THERE WITHOUT A RAFT?

IT'S BEAUTIFUL, BUT WHY CAN'T I UNDERSTAND WHAT THEY'RE SINGING?

IT'S ALL IN LATIN, SIR..

THEY MUST REALLY HATE US..

6-26

6-27

I THINK YOUR DOG HAS FINALLY FLIPPED..

WHAT'S HE DOING NOW?

GOOD EVENING..I'M ALISTAIR BEAGLE.. WE ARE NOW AT THE THIRD EPISODE OF "DARK AND STORMY NIGHT"

LOOK, THEY JUST SENT ME MY REPORT CARD FROM SUMMER SCHOOL.. I GOT THREE "A's"! DON'T TELL ME I'M NOT A GOOD STUDENT!

THIS ISN'T A REPORT CARD, SIR.. IT'S AN ADVERTISEMENT FOR THE "AAA PLUMBING COMPANY"

6-28

THERE MUST BE SOME MISTAKE..WE DIDN'T EVEN STUDY PLUMBING..

7-6

SORRY I MISSED THAT EASY FLY BALL, MANAGER

I THOUGHT I HAD IT, BUT SUDDENLY I REMEMBERED ALL THE OTHERS I'VE MISSED...

THE PAST GOT IN MY EYES!

7-7

I WONDER WHY I'M GOING TO THIS MOVIE

I WAS THINKING THE SAME THING

THOSE TWO GUYS ON TV HATED IT

WELL, WHO KNOWS?

MAYBE THERE'LL BE SOMETHING GOOD IN IT..

LIKE THE DOG TURNS OUT TO BE THE HERO

7-8

1989

A DOUBLE DIP CONE, PLEASE, WITH THE CHOCOLATE ON TOP AND THE VANILLA ON THE BOTTOM..

I LIKE THE VANILLA ON THE BOTTOM BECAUSE IT LEAVES A BETTER LINGERING AFTERTASTE..

THANK YOU.. I APPRECIATE THE PERFORMANCE OF A FINE CHEF

7-10

YOU DRIVE ME CRAZY!

I HAVE TO HAVE A BIBLE STORY TO TELL BY SUNDAY MORNING..

I WAS THINKING OF DANIEL IN THE 49 ers' DEN..

LIONS' DEN

7-11

WHATEVER

I HEAR YOUR GRANDFATHER HAS TAKEN UP GOLF

THAT'S RIGHT

7-12

HE'S BEEN PLAYING FOR ABOUT A YEAR..

THAT'S A LONG TIME TO BE OUT ON THE COURSE..

WELL, AREN'T YOU COMING?

IT DIDN'T SAY, "TROT"

STRIKE THREE!

Z

7-14

JUST WHAT I NEED..A PLAYER WHO STRIKES OUT WHILE HE'S ASLEEP!

HE'D BE EVEN MADDER IF HE KNEW I DREAMED I WAS HITTING A HOME RUN..

SOMETIMES, IF YOU PURPOSELY LOOK SAD, THEY'LL BRING YOU AN EXTRA BIG SUPPER...

HI, I NOTICED YOU APPEARED A BIT PEAKED..

I FIGURED YOU PROBABLY WEREN'T FEELING SO GOOD SO I DIDN'T GIVE YOU AS MUCH TO EAT..

7-15

AND SOMETIMES YOU DO SOMETHING THAT IS SO STUPID IT STAGGERS THE IMAGINATION!

WHO WAS ON THE PHONE?

A GIRL WHO SAID SHE WAS AN OLD FRIEND OF YOURS CALLING FROM OUT OF THE BLUE...

7-20

I DIDN'T KNOW WHERE THAT WAS SO I HUNG UP..

IT'S THAT SAME GIRL ON THE PHONE AGAIN..SHE SAYS SHE'S AN OLD FRIEND OF YOURS...

SHE INSISTS ON COMING OVER TO SEE YOU... SHE SAYS SHE HASN'T SEEN YOU FOR A LONG TIME...

I WARNED HER THAT SHE'LL PROBABLY BE DISAPPOINTED..

7-21

IT'S THAT GIRL AGAIN..SHE WANTS TO TALK TO YOU..

I WONDER WHAT SHE LOOKS LIKE

CAN YOU FIND OUT? BE SORT OF CAGEY.. BE SLY...

7-22

HE WANTS TO KNOW IF YOU'RE CUTE OR UGLY..

AAUGH!

OKAY, I'LL TELL HIM..

IT WAS THAT GIRL AGAIN..SHE WANTS YOU TO MEET HER OVER AT THE MALL

DO YOU THINK I SHOULD?

I DON'T KNOW..MAYBE IT'S A TRICK..MAYBE YOU SHOULD TAKE YOUR DOG ALONG..

AND IF YOU WANT, I'LL BRING MY SWORD CANE

I CAN'T BELIEVE I'M GOING OVER TO THE MALL TO MEET A GIRL I DON'T REMEMBER..

BUT MAYBE SHE'S REAL CUTE, AND MAYBE WE'LL FALL IN LOVE AND SOMEDAY GO OFF TO COLLEGE TOGETHER..

MAYBE SHE'LL PAT ME ON THE HEAD, AND I'LL TURN INTO A PIT BULL..

THIS MALL IS ENORMOUS.. HOW WILL THAT GIRL EVER FIND US?

MAYBE WE SHOULD JUST SIT ON THIS BENCH, AND HOPE SHE COMES BY AND SEES US...

WHILE WE'RE WAITING, I SHOULD HAVE A NEW PASSPORT PHOTO TAKEN..

THIS GIRL CALLS ON THE PHONE.. MY SISTER ANSWERS.. THE GIRL TELLS SALLY THAT SHE'S AN OLD FRIEND OF MINE...

HOW CAN THAT BE? I DON'T HAVE ANY OLD FRIENDS..I DON'T EVEN HAVE ANY NEW FRIENDS.. I DON'T UNDERSTAND...

CHARLIE BROWN!

OH, NO!

7-27

CHARLIE BROWN! OH, IT'S SO GOOD TO SEE YOU!

I'VE THOUGHT ABOUT YOU SO OFTEN!

7-28

ARE YOU SURE THERE HASN'T BEEN SOME MISTAKE?

WHO ARE YOU?

THIS IS A GREAT REUNION, CHARLIE BROWN! I THINK WE SHOULD GO CELEBRATE WITH A MARSHMALLOW SUNDAE!

WAIT! THERE'S SOMETHING YOU SHOULD KNOW!

7-29

DON'T TELL HER ANYTHING UNTIL AFTER THE MARSHMALLOW SUNDAE..

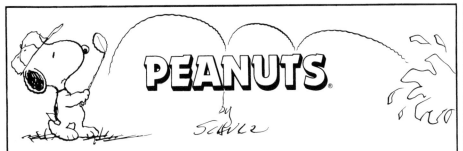

REMEMBER WHEN WE WERE AT CAMP, CHARLIE BROWN, AND WE'D SNEAK AWAY TO GET A MARSHMALLOW SUNDAE?

I'M NOT CHARLIE BROWN..I'M JUST A DOG...

I'VE THOUGHT ABOUT THOSE DAYS SO OFTEN...

SOMETIMES LIFE MAKES ME CONFUSED..

YOU'RE MORE CONFUSED THAN YOU THINK, SWEETIE..

7-31

8-1

WHO'S THE STUPID KID WHO KEEPS LOOKING AT US THROUGH THE WINDOW?

IF HE HAS A ROUND HEAD, I MAY KNOW HIM..

I CAN'T TELL YOU HOW NICE IT'S BEEN SEEING YOU AGAIN, CHARLIE BROWN..

ICE CREAM

MAYBE WE'LL SEE EACH OTHER AT CAMP AGAIN SOMEDAY...

8-2

ARE YOU SURE YOU'RE NOT MISTAKEN ABOUT SOMETHING?

WHO ARE YOU?

HOW COULD THAT GIRL THINK THAT YOU ARE ME?

SHE WAS REALLY STRANGE

I KIND OF LIKED HER..

SHE BOUGHT ME FIVE MARSHMALLOW SUNDAES, AND I ATE THEM ALL..OF COURSE, NOW, I DON'T FEEL SO GOOD...

8-3

8-4

YOU SURE FOOLED ME.. I THOUGHT "ROSEBUD" WAS HIS SKATEBOARD

YES, MA'AM..THESE ARE THE FOUR BOOKS OUR TEACHER WANTS US TO READ THIS SUMMER..

LIBRARY

OF COURSE, I'D BE THE LAST ONE TO BLAME YOU IF THEY'RE NOT IN..

YOU HAVE THEM ALL?!

8-5

THERE GOES MY FIRST EXCUSE..

LIBR

YEAH, OUR TEACHER EXPECTS US TO READ FOUR BOOKS THIS SUMMER..WEIRD, HUH?

WELL, JUST REMEMBER, WHEN YOU'RE READING, THE LIGHT SHOULD COME FROM OVER YOUR LEFT SHOULDER..

JUST THE EXCUSE I NEED, CHUCK... ALL THE LAMPS IN OUR HOUSE ARE ON THE WRONG SIDE!

8-7

CAN YOU IMAGINE OUR TEACHER EXPECTING US TO READ FOUR WHOLE BOOKS THIS SUMMER?

I MEAN, HOW ARE WE EVER GOING TO FIND TIME?

I READ MINE THE FIRST WEEK WE WERE HOME, SIR..

OH, SURE, MARCIE! OH, SURE! SURE, MARCIE! OH, SURE!

READ THEM ALL STRAIGHT ON THROUGH!

8-8

THESE ARE THE FOUR BOOKS I READ, SIR..BUT THEN I ALSO READ THIS EXTRA ONE...

"THE LITTLE PRINCE"... OH, WELL! LOOK HOW SHORT IT IS... WHAT'S SO GREAT ABOUT READING THIS?

8-9

I READ IT IN FRENCH, SIR

PEANUTS by SCHULZ

I HATE THAT PROGRAM!

WHO CARES?

WHY DO YOU ALWAYS WATCH SUCH STUPID PROGRAMS?

THEY'RE NOT AS STUPID AS THE DUMB RECORDS YOU LISTEN TO!

MY RECORDS AREN'T AS DUMB AS THE WEIRD COMIC BOOKS YOU READ!

WHAT DO YOU KNOW ABOUT READING?

OH, NO! NOW, WE'VE UPSET SNOOPY..

SEE? DOGS DON'T LIKE TO HEAR FAMILY ARGUMENTS.. IT MAKES THEM FEEL INSECURE...

WHERE DID HE GO?

8-13

PROBABLY IN THE CLOSET..

COME ON OUT, SNOOPY..EVERYTHING IS ALL RIGHT... WE'RE NOT FIGHTING ANYMORE..

BOO!

I CAN'T STAND IT!

8-24

POOR LOSER! POOR LOSER!

8-25

THAT SETTLES IT..NEXT TIME ONLY ONE OF YOU WILL BRING THE MARSHMALLOWS, AND HE'LL CARRY THEM IN A BOX!

LUCY! DO YOU THINK IF YOU PAID ATTENTION TO THE GAME, YOU MIGHT CATCH THE BALL JUST ONCE IN YOUR LIFE?!

SURE! CRITICIZE ME IN FRONT OF EVERYONE! SHOUT IT TO THE WHOLE WORLD!!

PSST... YOU'RE THE WORST PLAYER I'VE EVER SEEN!

8-26

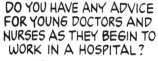

DOCTOR, DO YOU FIND THAT MAKING HOUSE CALLS HAS BECOME MORE DIFFICULT?

DEFINITELY

ESPECIALLY, WHEN YOU'RE NOT ALLOWED IN THE HOUSE..

I'M GOING TO BE IN A RACE TOMORROW.. I WONDER WHAT I SHOULD EAT BEFORE THE RACE..

I'D SUGGEST A TUNA SANDWICH..

IF YOU'RE GOING TO BE IN A RACE, ALWAYS EAT SOMETHING THAT SWIMS FAST

DOCTOR, I'VE BEEN WONDERING ABOUT EATING PASTA BEFORE A RACE...

WHAT IF YOU CAN'T FIND ANY PASTA?

THERE'S ALWAYS BOSTON CREAM PIE

PEANUTS by SCHULZ

MY REPORT? YES, MA'AM.. IT'S RIGHT HERE...

THIS IS HARD TO BELIEVE, BUT MY TOES ARE CAUGHT IN MY BINDER...

THE REPORT IS RIGHT IN THERE SOME-WHERE IF YOU CAN KIND OF GET IT OUT..THANK YOU..THAT WAS HARD ON MY TOES...

9-24

!

I HATE TO BOTHER YOU AGAIN, MA'AM, BUT I THINK MY SANDAL IS STUCK IN MY BINDER..

THANK YOU

DON'T SIGH LIKE THAT, MA'AM..CHRISTMAS VACATION IS A LONG WAY OFF..

MY DAD LIKES BEING A BARBER

HE SAYS IT'S TERRIBLE TO GO THROUGH LIFE WISHING YOU WERE SOMETHING ELSE

I NEVER WANTED TO BE ANYTHING BUT A DOG..

9-28

WHAT A MISERABLE DAY... EIGHT D-MINUSES WITH MORE TO COME..

MA'AM?

9-29

I'D LIKE PERMISSION TO GO TO THE PENCIL SHARPENER, THE DRINKING FOUNTAIN AND THE MOON

9-30

I THINK WHAT HAPPENS IS THAT SOMETIMES HE JUST GETS TIRED OF EATING ALONE..

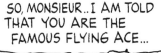

IT'S ALWAYS A PLEASURE TO TALK WITH A WORLD FAMOUS ATTORNEY..

AS YOU LOOK BACK UPON A LONG AND DISTINGUISHED CAREER, WHAT WOULD YOU SAY WAS THE MOST GRATIFYING CASE YOU EVER WON?

WON?

IS IT TRUE THAT YOU'VE BEEN PRACTICING LAW WITH A DOG LICENSE?

IT'S IMPOLITE TO ASK AN ATTORNEY SOMETHING THAT MAKES HIS HAT FLY OFF..

WE'VE BEEN READING POEMS IN SCHOOL, BUT I NEVER UNDERSTAND ANY OF THEM..

HOW AM I SUPPOSED TO KNOW WHICH POEMS TO LIKE?

SOMEBODY TELLS YOU

WHAT WOULD YOU SAY IF I TOLD YOU I WAS GOING TO DEVOTE THE REST OF MY LIFE TO MAKING YOU HAPPY?

WE'LL GO FOR LONG WALKS IN THE WOODS AND ROMP AROUND IN THE YARD...

YOU'LL SIT IN MY LAP, AND I'LL SCRATCH YOUR EARS, AND WE'LL WATCH TV AND I'LL GIVE YOU COOKIES...

WHAT KIND OF COOKIES?

10-26

YES, MA'AM...I'VE DECIDED TO QUIT SCHOOL.. I'LL PROBABLY NEVER AMOUNT TO ANYTHING ANYWAY...

I'M GOING TO DEVOTE THE REST OF MY LIFE TO MAKING MY DOG HAPPY..

10-27

NO, MA'AM, I HAVEN'T DISCUSSED THIS YET WITH MY MOTHER AND FATHER...

BUT I TALKED IT OVER WITH MY DOG, AND HE SEEMED TO THINK IT'S A GREAT IDEA..

BEFORE YOU DEVOTE THE REST OF YOUR LIFE TO MAKING YOUR DOG HAPPY, CHARLIE BROWN, LISTEN TO THIS..

IT'S BY RUDYARD KIPLING... "THERE IS SORROW ENOUGH IN THE NATURAL WAY.. WHY DO WE ALWAYS ARRANGE FOR MORE?"

10-28

" I BID YOU BEWARE OF GIVING YOUR HEART TO A DOG TO TEAR"

FORGET KIPLING... LET'S HAVE SOME MORE PIZZA!

HEY, YOU! GET OUTTA THERE!

MOM! DAD! THERE'S A PUMPKIN THIEF IN OUR PUMPKIN PATCH!

NO, WAIT! I'M NOT A THIEF! I'M GOING TO VIDEO THE "GREAT PUMPKIN" WHEN HE COMES..

HE SOUNDS LIKE HE'S CRAZY! AND HE'S GOT AN ATTACK DOG WITH HIM!

YOU SEE, ON HALLOWEEN NIGHT THE "GREAT PUMPKIN" RISES OUT OF THE...

YOU WANT A PUMPKIN, HUH?

WELL, HERE'S A PUMPKIN!

WUMP!

GOOD GRIEF!

10-29

I DID IT! I GOT THE "GREAT PUMPKIN" ON VIDEO!

I CAN'T STAND IT..

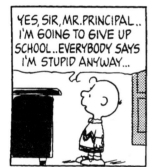

NO, MA'AM, I'VE NEVER TALKED TO A COUNSELOR BEFORE..

WELL, I'VE ALWAYS BEEN SORT OF A USELESS PERSON SO I THOUGHT I'D JUST DEVOTE THE REST OF MY LIFE TO MAKING MY DOG HAPPY...

I SUPPOSE YOU THINK I'M CRAZY..

REALLY? WHAT KIND OF A MONKEY DO YOU HAVE?

11-2

NO, MY BROTHER ISN'T HERE.. HE WENT TO THE MALL...

I THINK HE'S TRYING TO DO THINGS THAT WILL MAKE HIS STUPID DOG HAPPY..

11-3

BUNNIES! OOOH, I LOVE LOOKING AT THE BUNNIES!

PET SHOP

HEY, CHUCK, WHAT'S THIS ABOUT YOU QUITTING SCHOOL SO YOU CAN DEVOTE YOUR LIFE TO MAKING YOUR DOG HAPPY?

ASK HIM IF HE STILL LOVES ME

MARCIE WANTS TO KNOW WHY YOU DON'T DEVOTE YOUR LIFE TO MAKING HER HAPPY?

11-4

THAT'S NOT WHAT I SAID, SIR!

YEAH, WELL, SHE'S WEIRD, CHUCK..

HERE, HAVE ANOTHER COOKIE...

WE HAD A GOOD TIME TODAY, DIDN'T WE? HAVE I MADE YOU HAPPY?

I'D SAY I'M ABOUT ONE COOKIE AWAY FROM BEING HAPPY..

WE HAD A GOOD TIME AGAIN TODAY DIDN'T WE?

WE SURE DID..

IS THERE ANYTHING YOU'D LIKE TO DO TOMORROW?

MAYBE WE COULD TRY SOMETHING DIFFERENT..

TOMORROW LET'S HAVE THE JELLY DOUGHNUTS BEFORE THE PIZZA..

IT'S OUR NEW SCHOOL PRINCIPAL..HE SAYS YOU SHOULD COME BACK TO SCHOOL...

YES, SIR ..I'LL BE BACK TOMORROW..I'VE BEEN STAYING HOME TO MAKE MY DOG HAPPY...

WELL, HE ATE A LOT OF COOKIES AND STUFF YESTERDAY..

I THINK I HAPPIED HIM TO THE VET..

YES, SIR, IT'S GOOD TO BE BACK IN SCHOOL AGAIN.. I TRIED TO MAKE MY DOG HAPPY, BUT ALL I DID WAS MAKE HIM SICK...

11-9

YOU HAVEN'T MET MY DOG, HAVE YOU, SIR?

SNOOPY, THIS IS OUR NEW PRINCIPAL..

IT'D BE NICE, SIR, IF YOU RETURNED HIS SALUTE..

I REALLY THOUGHT I COULD DEVOTE MY WHOLE LIFE TO MAKING YOU HAPPY..

I'M SORRY IT DIDN'T WORK OUT

HEY, NO PROBLEM..

I WAS ALREADY HAPPY

11-10

TODAY IS VETERANS DAY..

I WONDER IF THERE'LL BE A LOT OF PARADES..

I THINK THERE SHOULD BE SOMETHING SPECIAL TO DO ON VETERANS DAY..

HERE'S THE WORLD WAR I FLYING ACE GOING OVER TO BILL MAULDIN'S HOUSE TO QUAFF A FEW ROOT BEERS..

11-11

EVERYTHING'S WRONG! I DON'T KNOW HOW I PUT UP WITH IT! AND IT'S GETTING WORSE! IT'S GETTING WORSE ALL THE TIME!

" HER VOICE WAS EVER SOFT, GENTLE, AND LOW..AN EXCELLENT THING IN WOMAN "

WHAT'D HE SAY?

11-13

Cooking Hints

When mixing dog food in a bowl, the water can either be put in first or added last.

Who cares?

11-14

YES, MA'AM.. I LEARNED A LOT TODAY...JUST BEING HERE WAS WORTH THE PRICE OF ADMISSION...

OF COURSE, I DIDN'T PAY ANYTHING!

HA HA HA HA HA HA!

11-15

YES, MA'AM

YOU'RE WEIRD, SIR..

WAKE ME WHEN THE SCHOOL BUS COMES..

HERE IT COMES NOW... IT'S ALMOST TO THE MIDDLE OF THE BLOCK..

YOU WOKE ME TOO SOON.. I COULD HAVE SLEPT ANOTHER THIRTY FEET...

UGH, MARCIE! HOW CAN YOU EAT THAT?

IT'S NOT NICE, SIR, TO MAKE DISPARAGING REMARKS ABOUT WHAT SOMEONE IS EATING!

ACTUALLY, IF YOU CAN'T SAY SOMETHING NICE, YOU SHOULDN'T SAY ANYTHING AT ALL...

YOU HAVE A CUTE LUNCH, MARCIE..

SHOVEL YOUR WALK?

SHOVEL OUR WALK?! IT ISN'T EVEN SNOWING!

November

1989

WHEN YOU LIVE ALONE IN THE DESERT, NO ONE INVITES YOU OVER FOR THANKSGIVING..

YOU HAVE TO PRETEND YOU'RE HAVING YOUR OWN TURKEY DINNER...

11-23

NO MATTER HOW HARD YOU PRETEND, A ROCK IS STILL A ROCK..

I WENT INTO A STORE YESTERDAY TO TRY ON A PATHETIC HELMET...

THE CLERK SAID, "YOU MUST MEAN A 'PITH' HELMET"

11-24

AFTER I PUT ONE ON, HE SAID, "MAYBE YOU WERE RIGHT.."

"ON YOU IT LOOKS PATHETIC!"

IF YOU WEAR A PITH HELMET IN THE DESERT, YOU LOOK LIKE A LEADER..

11-25

EVERYONE TREATS YOU WITH MORE RESPECT

I THINK

PEANUTS.
by SCHULZ

LISTEN TO
THE THUNDER..

I'M GLAD WE'RE INSIDE..THIS IS
THE WORST STORM I'VE EVER SEEN..

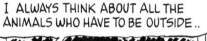

I ALWAYS THINK ABOUT ALL THE
ANIMALS WHO HAVE TO BE OUTSIDE..

AND THE
BIRDS..

THAT'S RIGHT..BIRDS, AND
DEER, AND SQUIRRELS,
AND RABBITS..

AND STRAY
CATS..

AND HORSES,
AND COWS, AND
LITTLE BUGS..

11-26

NO, I DON'T THINK WE
CAN GO OUT AND
RESCUE ALL OF THEM

WHY DO I HAVE THE FEELING THAT SOMEONE HAS JUST THROWN A SNOWBALL AT ME?

IF THAT SNOWBALL HITS ME, THE PERSON WHO THREW IT IS GOING TO REGRET IT FOR THE REST OF HIS LIFE!

SMART! VERY, VERY SMART!

THE FAMOUS WORLD WAR I
FLYING ACE LOOKS LONELY..

WOULD IT HELP IF I HELD
HIS PAW FOR AWHILE?

LIKE MAYBE
UNTIL 1918?

C'MON, CHUCK.. ANSWER THE PHONE

HELLO?

HI, CHUCK.. DO YOU HAVE A PENCIL HANDY?

NO, BUT I CAN GET ONE..

WE HAVE A NEW PHONE NUMBER.. I JUST WANT TO GIVE IT TO YOU

ASK HIM IF HE STILL LOVES ME

FROM NOW ON THAT'S OUR NUMBER.. DID YOU GET IT?

ASK HIM IF HE EVER THINKS ABOUT ME...

12-31

I'M NOT SURE I CAN REMEMBER IT

DIDN'T YOU WRITE IT DOWN? I TOLD YOU TO GET A PENCIL...

I DON'T HAVE ANY PAPER.. YOU DIDN'T SAY ANYTHING ABOUT PAPER...

CHUCK, YOU BLOCK-HEAD!

ASK HIM IF HE STILL THINKS I'M CUTE...

FORGET IT, CHUCK! DON'T CALL ME.. I'LL CALL YOU... LIKE IN A HUNDRED YEARS!

YOU DIDN'T ASK HIM

1989

IS THIS THE TOUR BUS TO STONEHENGE?

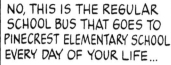

NO, THIS IS THE REGULAR SCHOOL BUS THAT GOES TO PINECREST ELEMENTARY SCHOOL EVERY DAY OF YOUR LIFE...

1-8

HOW DID I GET ON THE WRONG BUS?

1-9

SHOVEL YOUR WALK?

I'M TRYING TO SAVE UP MONEY FOR COLLEGE...

1-10

MY BADMINTON SCHOLARSHIP FELL THROUGH..

I WASN'T SURE I HEARD A DOUGHNUT CALLING ME...

BUT THEN I SAW A LUNCH BOX WALK BY..

I HEARD THE TEACHER, SIR.. SHE SAID YOUR REPORT SOUNDED LIKE YOU WROTE IT ON THE SCHOOL BUS...

I WAS FLATTERED, MARCIE...

ACTUALLY, I WROTE IT AFTER I GOT OFF THE BUS, AND WAS WALKING UP THE STAIRS INTO SCHOOL..

"Help! Am stranded in some stupid dog's water dish!
A bug

YOU'RE WELCOME.. BUT I DIDN'T CARE FOR THE PART ABOUT THE STUPID DOG!

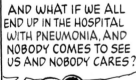

PEANUTS by Schulz

IT HAPPENED AGAIN LAST NIGHT..

OF COURSE, I EXPECTED IT..

WHENEVER MOM AND DAD COME HOME, AS SOON AS THEY PULL INTO THE DRIVEWAY, MOM SAYS, "HOME AGAIN, FINNIGIN"

"HOME AGAIN, FINNIGIN"?

GRAMMA USED TO SAY IT, TOO...

ALL FAMILIES HAVE TRADITIONS..SOME OF THEM ALWAYS GO TO THE MOUNTAINS IN THE SUMMER..SOME FAMILIES ALWAYS GO TO HAWAII FOR THE HOLIDAYS...

SOME FAMILIES ALWAYS HAVE A BIG DINNER ON SUNDAY..SOME FAMILIES ALWAYS GO TO THE OPERA ON OPENING NIGHT...

ALL FAMILIES HAVE TRADITIONS..

1-21

OUR FAMILY SAYS, "HOME AGAIN, FINNIGIN"

SURE, WHY NOT?

WELL, PUT IT ON, AND LET ME SEE...

YES, IT DOES MAKE YOU LOOK TALLER

I WONDER WHAT I CAN DO TO MAKE THAT LITTLE RED-HAIRED GIRL NOTICE ME..

MAYBE IF I WALK AROUND THE ROOM A BIT...I'LL BET SHE NOTICES ME NOW...

ESPECIALLY AFTER I GET MY SLEEVE CAUGHT IN THE PENCIL SHARPENER..

IF THAT LITTLE RED-HAIRED GIRL SEES ME STANDING HERE WITH MY SLEEVE CAUGHT IN THE PENCIL SHARPENER, SHE'LL THINK I'M THE DUMBEST PERSON IN THE WORLD

WHAT I HAVE TO DO IS WRIGGLE OUT OF MY SWEATER BUT STILL LOOK REAL COOL...

I'VE BEEN WONDERING WHEN IT WAS THAT DOGS FIRST BEGAN TO BE REGARDED AS MAN'S BEST FRIEND...

PROBABLY RIGHT AFTER THE INVENTION OF COOKIES

1-29

YES, MA'AM, I'D LIKE PERMISSION TO LEAVE EARLY..MY DOG IS EXPECTING ME HOME

1-30

SOMETIMES HE HAS BAD DREAMS AND NEEDS COMFORTING...

WHAT DID SHE SAY, CHARLIE BROWN?

WELL, SHE STARTED OFF BY SAYING SOMETHING ABOUT "IN ALL HER YEARS OF TEACHING," AND THEN I MISSED THE LAST PART...

DOG BREAK!

YES, MA'AM..A "DOG BREAK" IS WHEN YOU GET TO GO HOME TO SEE IF YOUR DOG MISSES YOU OR NEEDS YOU FOR ANYTHING...

1-31

NICE TRY..

YOU'RE RIGHT..
WE SHOULD HAVE
HAD A PICTURE
OF THAT..

YOUR NEW HAIRDO IS SORT
OF IN MY FACE, SIR...

I CAN'T HEAR YOU, MA'AM..
THERE'S AN ECHO IN HERE...

SO WE'RE RIDING
ALONG IN THE CAR,
SEE...

JUST AS WE COME TO
A STOPLIGHT, A PICKUP
TRUCK PULLS ALONGSIDE
WITH A BIG DOG IN
THE BACK...

THE STUPID DOG
BARKED AT ME!

I WAS OFFENDED

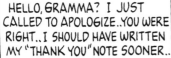

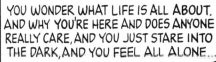

1990

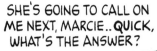

PEANUTS

by Schulz

PAWPET
SHOW
TODAY

PAWPET
SHOW
←

NOW
PLAYING
"PAWPETS
ON ICE"

GOOD SHOW,
ISN'T IT?

REMINDS YOU OF
PEGGY FLEMING
AND RICHARD DWYER,
DOESN'T IT?

2-25

BUT I THOUGHT IT WAS
AN ICE SHOW...

WHERE'S
THE
ICE?

YOU HAVEN'T CALLED US IN A LONG WHILE, CHUCK..DON'T YOU LIKE US ANYMORE?

OR MAYBE YOU NEVER DID LIKE US..IS THAT TRUE, CHUCK? THAT YOU NEVER DID LIKE US? HUH, CHUCK? HUH?

WE'RE SORRY..THE NUMBER YOU HAVE CALLED IS NO LONGER IN SERVICE..IT WAS A MINUTE AGO, BUT THESE THINGS HAPPEN..

THIS IS MY REPORT ON THE WIND...

WIND BLOWS YOUR HAIR AROUND WHEN YOU'RE WALKING TO SCHOOL, AND AFTER YOU GET THERE, YOU DON'T HAVE A COMB..

IT ALSO GIVES YOU SOMETHING TO WRITE ABOUT WHEN YOU CAN'T THINK OF ANYTHING ELSE, AND YOU CAN'T SEE WHAT YOU'RE READING...

WHERE'S EVERYBODY GOING? THIS IS ONLY A SHOWER!

C'MON! WE NEED THE PRACTICE! ARE YOU AFRAID OF A LITTLE RAIN?!!

3-8

CHARLIE BROWN, AT WHAT POINT DOES A MANAGER KNOW HIS TEAM IS IN TROUBLE?

3-9

WHEN HIS PLAYERS TROT OUT ONTO THE FIELD, AND ONE OF THEM TRIPS OVER SECOND BASE

DO YOU KNOW WHAT IT'S LIKE TO LOSE A BALL GAME BY ONE RUN IN THE NINTH INNING?!

NO, I CAN'T SAY THAT I DO

NEITHER DO I...

WE LOST BY FORTY RUNS IN FIVE INNINGS!

3-10

I'M AWAKE!

YES, MA'AM.. WELL, THAT MIGHT BE HARD TO ANSWER..

3-11

I MEAN, IT WOULD BE COMPARING APPLES AND EGGS..

ORANGES

YES, ORANGES AND EGGS...

APPLES AND ORANGES...

OR EGGS AND PUMPKINS!

PUMPKINS AND CELERY!

CARROTS AND COCONUTS!

GRAPES AND CUCUMBERS!

BANANAS AND RADISHES!

YES, MA'AM

YOU'RE WEIRD, SIR, BUT YOU'RE A LOT OF FUN

PRINCIPAL'S OFFICE

THEY SAY IF TWO PEOPLE LIVE TOGETHER LONG ENOUGH, THEY BEGIN TO LOOK ALIKE

3-12

WHAT DO YOU MEAN, YOU HOPE NOT?

3-13

HAVE YOU EVER NOTICED HOW, AT THIS TIME OF YEAR, THE RAYS OF THE SUN REFLECT OFF THE SHINY WHITE PAINT ON THE "OUT OF BOUNDS" STAKES?

TRUE! FALSE! TRUE! MAYBE! WHO KNOWS? WHY NOT? COULD BE! TRUE AGAIN!

ABSOLUTELY FALSE! A SURE THING! NOW AND THEN! WHO CARES? TRUE AGAIN!

3-14

IF THE GOOD LORD IS WILLING, AND THE CREEKS DON'T RISE!

YOU'RE REALLY WEIRD, SIR

March

I'VE OFTEN WONDERED WHY YOU DECIDED TO BECOME A CACTUS WHEN YOU MIGHT HAVE BEEN AN ORANGE TREE..

NO, THAT'S ALL RIGHT..

I CAN UNDERSTAND YOUR NOT WANTING TO DISCUSS IT..

3-15

DOES YOUR GRAMPA PLAY MUCH GOLF THESE DAYS?

HE SAYS HE PLAYS MOSTLY IN HIS HEAD...

3-16

BUT HE SAYS THE COURSE IS TOO NARROW..

3-17

FLAG MAN AHEAD

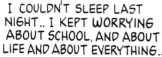

WHAT KIND OF A SHORTSTOP ARE YOU?! THAT BALL WENT RIGHT BY YOU, AND YOU DIDN'T EVEN MOVE!

3-29
YOU DIDN'T SAY, "FETCH"

3-30
QUICK, MARCIE, I NEED THE ANSWER TO THE THIRD QUESTION!

THERE IS NO THIRD QUESTION, SIR..WE DID THAT TEST LAST WEEK...

TIME FLIES WHEN YOU'RE HAVING FUN..

COME ON, CHARLIE BROWN.. STRIKE THIS GUY OUT! YOU CAN DO IT! WE BELIEVE IN YOU!
3-31

I'VE ALWAYS BELIEVED IN YOU..

HYPOCRITE THAT I AM..

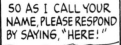

YOU WERE SITTING THERE IN YOUR BOOTH, AND I WAS SITTING RIGHT HERE WHERE I AM NOW...

THE DOCTOR

PSYCHIATRIC HELP 5¢

THE DOCTOR IS IN

AND I REMEMBER WHAT YOU TOLD ME..

YOU SAID THAT WHEN I BECOME DEPRESSED, I SHOULD ALWAYS REMEMBER THAT "EVERY CLOUD HAS A SILVER LINING"

I WANT YOU TO LOOK AT THIS...

THE DOCTOR IS IN

HMM..VERY INTERESTING

I THINK I SEE THE PROBLEM...

4-8

HELP 5¢

WHAT WE HAVE HERE IS A DEFECTIVE CLOUD..

THE DOCTOR

WELL, MA'AM, I DIDN'T HAVE ANY WRITING PAPER...

SO I DID MY HOMEWORK ON A PAPER PLATE..

4-9

DIDN'T CARE FOR IT, HUH, MA'AM?

I'M WAITING FOR A SCHOOL BUS THAT WILL TAKE ME TO SCHOOL..AND FOR WHAT?

TO GET ON ANOTHER BUS, AND GO ON A FIELD TRIP TO SOME STUPID PLACE I'VE NEVER HEARD OF! I CAN'T STAND IT!

4-10

I SHOULD HAVE STAYED IN PRE-SCHOOL..

WHY ARE WE GOING ON A FIELD TRIP WHEN IT'S GOING TO RAIN?

WHAT MAKES YOU THINK IT'S GOING TO RAIN? OUR TEACHER SAID IT'S GOING TO BE A NICE DAY...

FIELD TRIPS CAUSE RAIN..

4-11

1990

HERE..IF YOU WEAR THIS CROWN, EVERYONE WILL THINK YOU'RE KING OF THE JUNGLE!

WELL, FROM A DISTANCE THEY'LL NEVER KNOW IT'S CARDBOARD

NOW, GO OUT THERE, AND SHOW EVERYONE THAT YOU'RE THE KING OF THE JUNGLE!

WELL, SURE..YOU MAY HAVE TO CROSS THE STREET..

MAKE WAY FOR THE KING OF THE JUNGLE!

I ALWAYS THOUGHT THE LION WAS THE KING OF THE JUNGLE...

4-19

MAKE WAY FOR THE NEW IMPROVED KING OF THE JUNGLE!

SO I FIGURED IF YOU'RE GOING TO BE KING OF THE JUNGLE, YOU SHOULD HAVE A THRONE..AND I THINK I'VE FOUND ONE

4-20

IF SOMEONE COMES ALONG TO WAIT FOR A BUS, YOU MAY HAVE TO MOVE OVER A LITTLE BIT..

YOU'VE DECIDED YOU DON'T WANT TO BE KING OF THE JUNGLE?

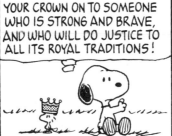

THEN YOU SHOULD PASS YOUR CROWN ON TO SOMEONE WHO IS STRONG AND BRAVE, AND WHO WILL DO JUSTICE TO ALL ITS ROYAL TRADITIONS!

IT JUST FITS..

4-21

I DON'T BELIEVE IT..YOU'VE BEEN SELECTED FOR JURY DUTY!

THIS IS RIDICULOUS! DON'T THEY KNOW YOU'RE A DOG?

WHAT'S WRONG WITH THAT?

4-30

OBVIOUSLY, THERE'S BEEN A MISTAKE..

I'LL GO IF THEY GIVE AWAY FREE COOKIES..

5-1

ACCORDING TO THIS, YOU'VE BEEN SELECTED FOR JURY DUTY...

"FAILURE TO RESPOND CAN RESULT IN ATTACHMENT AND FINE"

I DON'T THINK I COULD EVER DO HARD TIME..

YES, MA'AM, I'M CALLING ABOUT MY DOG..APPARENTLY YOU'VE SELECTED HIM FOR JURY DUTY...

ASK HER IF THEY GIVE FREE COOKIES

5-2

NO, MA'AM, I'M NOT CALLING FOR MYSELF...I'M CALLING FOR MY DOG... I THINK THERE'S BEEN A MISTAKE..

PARKING? NO, MA'AM, I'M NOT CALLING ABOUT PARKING.. I'M...HELLO? HELLO?

YOU DIDN'T ASK HER ABOUT THE COOKIES..

YES, MA'AM? US? THE JUDGE WANTS TO SEE **US**?!

WHY WOULD THE JUDGE WANT TO SEE **US**?

HE PROBABLY WANTS MY OPINION ON SOME OBSCURE POINT OF LAW..

5-7

YES, SIR...NO, YOUR HONOR, I'VE NEVER MET A JUDGE BEFORE..

WELL, MY DOG GOT THIS CARD IN THE MAIL SAYING HE HAD BEEN SELECTED FOR JURY DUTY, AND...

THIS IS A NICE ROOM..IT REMINDS ME OF THE TIME I WAS CALLED IN TO ADVISE GENERAL PERSHING...

5-8

SO THEN WHAT HAPPENED?

THEN THE JUDGE APOLOGIZED TO US FOR THE MIS-UNDERSTANDING, AND SAID WE WERE GOOD CITIZENS FOR TRYING TO DO WHAT WAS RIGHT..

I WAS ALL SET TO VOTE 'GUILTY'!

5-9

1990

5-14

THERE'S NO HURRY, I GUESS, BUT LET ME KNOW WHEN I CAN HAVE YOUR SUPPER DISH...

THIS IS THE REPORT I'M GIVING TOMORROW ON VOLCANOES...

"LIFE IN THE VILLAGE WAS PEACEFUL UNTIL THE VOLCANO INTERRUPTED"

HOW IMPOLITE

WHAT DID YOU SAY?

I SAID, IT SOUNDS LIKE A GOOD REPORT

I'LL GO READ IT TO YOUR DOG..

5-16

I THOUGHT MAYBE I WAS THUMBIDEXTROUS, BUT I GUESS I'M NOT..

PEANUTS by Schulz

"AND THOSE ARE OUR SCORES"

WHAT DO YOU MEAN, THOSE ARE YOUR SCORES?!

THEY DID IT AGAIN! THEY DIDN'T SAY A THING ABOUT WOMEN'S SPORTS!

ALL THOSE GAMES AND NOT ONE MENTION OF A WOMAN!

I'M GONNA GET ON A BUS, MARCIE, AND GO DOWN TO THAT TV STATION AND COMPLAIN!

EVERY SPORTS SHOW IS THE SAME! MEN, MEN, MEN! NEVER ANY WOMEN'S SPORTS!

WE WANNA SPEAK TO THE MANAGER OF THIS TV STATION..

WE'VE COME TO COMPLAIN ABOUT YOUR SPORTS BROADCASTS! YOU NEVER GIVE THE SCORES OF WOMEN'S SPORTS! IT'S ALWAYS MEN! WHAT ABOUT WOMEN?!

THAT WAS ODD, WASN'T IT, SIR?

WHAT WAS ODD?

THE STATION MANAGER WAS A WOMAN..

REALLY? I DIDN'T EVEN NOTICE..

OUR BUS DRIVER IS A WOMAN, TOO, SIR..

ASK HER WHAT THE SCORE IS, MARCIE..

BUS STOP

5-20

INSTEAD OF GOING TO SUMMER CAMP, I'VE DECIDED TO STAY HOME AND WORK ON MY STAMP COLLECTION..

YOU DON'T HAVE A STAMP COLLECTION

5-24

THAT'S A RELIEF!

WELL, IT SOUNDS LIKE AN INTERESTING SUMMER CAMP, BUT I HAVEN'T DECIDED YET..

YES, CANOEING, SWIMMING, ROCK CLIMBING, TENNIS, HIKING, SOCCER..ALL OF THOSE THINGS...YOU ARE?

5-25

GRANDMA SAYS SHE'S GOING..

SOMETIMES, WHEN YOU'RE WAITING FOR YOUR SUPPER, IT'S BEST TO ACT REAL COOL..

IF YOU ACT LIKE YOU DON'T REALLY CARE, ALL OF A SUDDEN YOU CAN TURN AROUND, AND..

..THERE IT IS!!

SOMETIMES

5-26

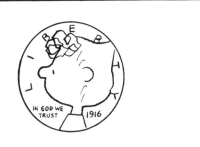

HERE'S THE WORLD FAMOUS NATURALIST GOING OUT ON A BIRD-COUNTING WALK...

5-28

THERE'S ONE!!

WOODSTOCK HATES BIRD-COUNTING JOKES..

"IN 1066, NAPOLEON CROSSED THE MISSISSIPPI RIVER"

5-29

I'LL BET THE TEACHER HAS FUN CORRECTING YOUR TEST PAPERS, SIR..

SHE PROBABLY HAS FRIENDS OVER, AND MAKES IT INTO A BIG PARTY..

YOU'RE WEIRD, MARCIE

5-30

YES, MA'AM..MARCIE SAYS SHE THINKS YOU LAUGH AT MY ANSWERS ON THE TESTS YOU GIVE US...

I DON'T THINK THAT'S NICE, MA'AM..

WELL, IF NAPOLEON HAD SEEN THE MISSISSIPPI, I'LL BET HE WOULD HAVE CROSSED IT!

1990

DID I TELL YOU I GOT A GRANT FROM THE NATIONAL ENDOWMENT FOR THE ARTS?

WESTERN PAINTINGS FOR SALE

5-31

YOU CAN'T DO MUCH, THOUGH, WITH THIRTY-FIVE CENTS

LOOK, MARCIE, I PASSED! I GOT A PASSING GRADE IN EVERY SUBJECT!

"SLEEPING, DRINKING FOUNTAIN, LUNCH AND DAYDREAMING!" CONGRATULATIONS, SIR!

6-1

IT'S NOT POLITE TO MAKE FUN OF PEOPLE, MARCIE..

I'M ONE OF YOUR GREATEST ADMIRERS, SIR!

I'M GOING INTO NEEDLES TO TRY TO SELL ONE OF MY WESTERN PAINTINGS..

MAYBE SOME WEALTHY LANDOWNER WILL BE INTERESTED...

6-2

..OR SOME LITTLE KID WHO HAS FIFTY CENTS

1990

Page 225

YES, MA'AM, I KNOW WHY I'M IN SUMMER SCHOOL...

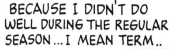

BECAUSE I DIDN'T DO WELL DURING THE REGULAR SEASON...I MEAN TERM..

6-11

WHATEVER..

STUDY HARD IN SUMMER SCHOOL TODAY, SIR..

6-12

WAKE ME UP WHEN YOU COME BY HERE AGAIN ON YOUR WAY HOME..

IF I HIT HER WITH THIS LITTLE BOOK OF POEMS, SHE MIGHT NOT FEEL IT..

I'D BETTER USE "WAR AND PEACE"

ALL I'M DOING IS SITTING ON YOUR BLANKET.. IF YOU TRY TO PULL IT AWAY, I'LL SUE YOU FOR ANIMAL CRUELTY!

KEEP THE BLANKET.. I'M GOING INTO THE KITCHEN, AND MAKE MYSELF A CHOCOLATE SUNDAE...

NOW, **THAT'S** ANIMAL CRUELTY!

6-13

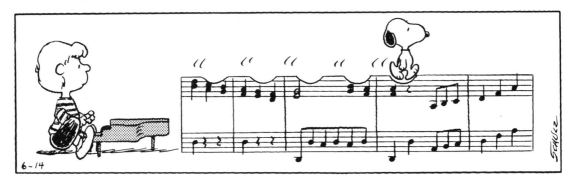

I HAVE TO CALL MY TEACHER AT SUMMER SCHOOL AND TELL HER I WON'T BE THERE TODAY...

DON'T YOU HAVE TO LOOK UP HER NUMBER?

NO, I JUST DIAL "D-MINUS"

BEETHOVEN NEVER WON THE FRENCH OPEN, WIMBLEDON, OR THE STANLEY CUP...

KLUNK

PROBABLY COULDN'T STAND CRITICISM, EITHER..

YES, MA'AM, I'M ENJOYING SUMMER SCHOOL..

I BELIEVE IT'S BEEN GOOD FOR ME...

6-21

IT SAVES A LOT ON SUNSCREEN

HI, MARCIE.. I JUST GOT HOME FROM SUMMER SCHOOL..WHAT'VE YOU BEEN DOIN'?

WELL, CHARLES AND I HAVE BEEN SITTING HERE MOST OF THE DAY JUST WATCHING TV, AND....CHARLES! I CAN'T EAT POPCORN IF YOU'RE HOLDING MY HAND! PLEASE, CHARLES! ..AND WE...CHARLES, PLEASE! AND WE...

I'LL CALL YOU AGAIN SOMETIME WHEN I'M HOME FROM COLLEGE, MARCIE!

6-22

I WAS ONLY TEASING YOU YESTERDAY, SIR.. CHARLES AND I WEREN'T REALLY TOGETHER...

YOU HAD ME PRETTY UPSET, MARCIE..

GETTING UPSET IS GOOD FOR YOU, SIR.. IT PREPARES YOU FOR ALL THE THINGS THAT ARE GOING TO HAPPEN TO YOU LATER IN LIFE...

6-23

YOU'RE A JOY TO BE WITH, MARCIE

"RULE 28...BALL UNPLAYABLE.."

6-25

HI, MARCIE..I'M HOME... TODAY WAS OUR LAST DAY OF SUMMER SCHOOL..

DID YOU LEARN ANYTHING?

6-26

THE WATER IN THE DRINKING FOUNTAIN WAS ALWAYS WARM

HI, CHUCK..JUST THOUGHT I'D DROP BY, AND LET YOU KNOW I'M ALL THROUGH WITH SUMMER SCHOOL...

I DIDN'T KNOW YOU HAD BEEN GOING TO SUMMER SCHOOL..

6-27

THANKS, CHUCK..GLAD TO SEE YOU'RE KEEPING UP WITH WHAT YOUR FRIENDS ARE DOING..

AUNT MARION WAS RIGHT..NEVER MARRY A MUSICIAN AND NEVER ANSWER THE DOOR..

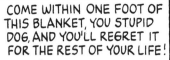

SCULPTURE BY CAMILLE LUCY CLAUDEL

THAT'S A NICE LOOKING CASTLE

THIS IS MORE THAN A CASTLE.. THIS IS THE KING'S CASTLE...

WELL, THAT'S ALMOST AS GOOD...

ALMOST?

ALMOST AS GOOD AS WHAT?

ALMOST AS GOOD AS THE QUEEN'S THRONE!

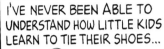

IF YOU HAD SHOES TO TIE, YOU WOULDN'T THINK THIS WAS SO FUNNY...

WHY DON'T YOU GET SOME SHOES? MICKEY MOUSE WEARS SHOES...

MICKEY MOUSE'S SHOES DON'T HAVE LACES..

7-5

IT'S EMBARRASSING! CAN YOU IMAGINE? I'VE FORGOTTEN HOW TO TIE MY OWN SHOES!

7-6

ANYWAY, I GUESS I'LL GO HOME..

WHY SO SOON?

IT'S HARD STANDING AROUND ON THE SIDEWALK IN YOUR BARE FEET..

I THINK WHAT HAPPENED WAS I GOT USED TO TYING MY SHOES WITHOUT THINKING..

7-7

SO WHEN I STARTED TO THINK ABOUT IT, I COULDN'T DO IT...

DOES THAT MAKE SENSE?

HOW ABOUT STUPIDITY?

I TALKED TO HER, LINUS! WE WERE STANDING IN LINE TOGETHER, AND I TALKED TO HER!

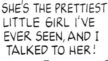

SHE'S THE PRETTIEST LITTLE GIRL I'VE EVER SEEN, AND I TALKED TO HER!

OH, I GUESS I DIDN'T TELL YOU.. THIS IS ME, LINUS... I'M CALLING AGAIN FROM CAMP...

I KIND OF FIGURED IT WAS YOU, CHARLIE BROWN..

7-26

NOW THAT WE'VE HAD LUNCH TOGETHER, I CAN TELL YOU MY NAME IS PEGGY JEAN...

WELL, UH...UH...MY NAME IS...UH...UH..MY NAME IS.. UH..BROWNIE CHARLES!

7-27

THAT'S CUTE.. I LIKE IT..

MAYBE I'LL JUST JUMP INTO THE LAKE RIGHT HERE

AND THEN, LINUS, I GOT SO NERVOUS TRYING TO TELL HER MY NAME, I SAID IT WAS "BROWNIE CHARLES"...

HA HA HA HA!! CHARLIE BROWN, YOU ARE REALLY SOMETHING!

7-28

NOW SHE CALLS ME "BROWNIE CHARLES" ALL THE TIME...BUT YOU KNOW WHAT?

I KIND OF LIKE IT..

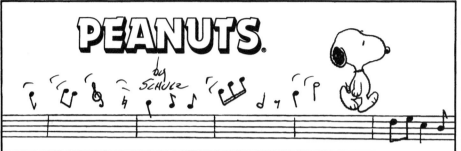

WHERE DID SHE GO? PEGGY JEAN? WHERE ARE YOU?!

HEY, IS YOUR NAME BROWNIE CHARLES? WHAT A WEIRD NAME... ANYWAY, A GIRL ASKED ME IF I'D GIVE YOU THIS NOTE...

"DEAR BROWNIE CHARLES, YOU NEVER TRUSTED ME, DID YOU? I THOUGHT YOU LIKED ME... I'M GOING HOME.."

THAT HAPPENED TO ME ONCE WITH A GOLDEN RETRIEVER..

8-6

PEGGY JEAN IS GONE, LINUS! SHE GOT MAD! SHE SAID I DIDN'T TRUST HER

I LOVED HER, LINUS, AND NOW I'LL NEVER SEE HER AGAIN...

8-7

GOLF IS A CRUEL GAME, CHARLIE BROWN

WHAT'S THAT GOT TO DO WITH IT?

IT'S ALL I COULD THINK OF TO SAY..

I REALLY LOVED THAT PRETTY LITTLE GIRL.. AND NOW SHE'S GONE...

SHE ALWAYS CALLED ME "BROWNIE CHARLES." I'D GIVE ANYTHING TO HEAR THAT AGAIN...

WOOF!

8-8

WELL, YEAH... SORT OF LIKE THAT..

Dear Peggy Jean, I miss you very much.

WHY BOTHER TO WRITE? SHE'LL NEVER REMEMBER YOU..YOU'RE THE KIND OF PERSON WHO IS EASY TO FORGET...

I'M YOUR COUSIN, AND EVEN I CAN'T REMEMBER YOU..

SISTER! WHATEVER

8-13

MY GRAMPA HAD ANOTHER BIRTHDAY YESTERDAY..

8-14

HE SAID," I HAVE TO ADMIT THAT THE YEARS HAVE BEEN GOOD TO ME"

" BUT THE MONTHS AND WEEKS HAVE BEEN A LITTLE RUDE!"

HEY, MANAGER, IT'S TOO HOT TO PLAY TODAY!

8-15

WHAT MAKES YOU THINK IT'S ANY HOTTER NOW THAN IT ALWAYS IS?

I DON'T KNOW..JUST A FEELING, I GUESS..

PEANUTS.
by SCHULZ

192673

192674

RAFFLE TICKETS? SURE, I'LL BUY SOME..

ANYTHING TO HELP THE BEAGLE SCOUTS...WAIT'LL I GET SOME MONEY..

HERE, I'LL TAKE THIRTY...

8-19

HEY, WAIT A MINUTE! WHAT DO I WIN IF I HAVE THE WINNING TICKET?

WHAT'S THIS?

" YOU DON'T WIN ANYTHING, BUT YOU'LL HAVE THE PLEASURE OF OWNING YOUR VERY OWN RAFFLE TICKETS.. BE THE FIRST ON YOUR BLOCK TO START A COLLECTION "

STUPID BEAGLE!

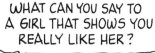

THE MAILMAN DID IT AGAIN! HE KEEPS LEAVING US LETTERS ADDRESSED TO "BROWNIE CHARLES"

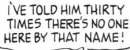
I'VE TOLD HIM THIRTY TIMES THERE'S NO ONE HERE BY THAT NAME!

THOSE LETTERS WERE FOR ME! THAT'S WHAT PEGGY JEAN CALLS ME! I'M "BROWNIE CHARLES"!!

NO, YOU'RE NOT.. YOU'RE WEIRD..

Dear Peggy Jean,
I'm sorry that all your letters were returned to you.

SOMEDAY WE'LL LAUGH ABOUT ALL THIS...

HA!

NO, SOMEDAY..

LOOK! I GOT A LETTER FROM PEGGY JEAN.. SHE SAYS SHE MISSES ME..

SHE SAYS SHE HOPES WE MEET AGAIN SOMETIME..

I'LL BET THAT ISN'T ALL

SHE ALSO SAYS, "GIVE A HUG TO YOUR CUTE, WONDERFUL, CHARMING, LITTLE DOG"

I KNEW IT

PEANUTS by Schulz

"TEAL"?

"TEAL" OR "CERULEAN"...WHICH COLOR EXPRESSES WHAT I'M TRYING TO SAY HERE?

DOES "WILD STRAWBERRY" SAY ANYTHING AT ALL?

AND I'M NOT SURE IF "FUCHSIA" MAKES AN EFFORT TO COMMUNICATE..

9-2

WHICH REALLY SPEAKS LOUDER, "TANGERINE" OR "DANDELION"?

IN FACT, DOES "ROYAL PURPLE" SAY WHAT WE...

COLOR THE SKY BLUE AND THE GRASS GREEN!

GET OUT THE "BLACK".. I'LL DO A NIGHT SCENE..

SCHOOL STARTS TOMORROW, MARCIE.. I NEED TO BORROW A NOTEBOOK, SOME PAPER, A RULER AND A PENCIL...

HAS IT EVER OCCURRED TO YOU, SIR, THAT THOSE ITEMS CAN BE PURCHASED AT YOUR NEAREST STORE?

9-3

DON'T ASK ME TO BE MAID OF HONOR AT YOUR WEDDING, MARCIE..

9-4

SORRY, MA'AM..THE FIRST QUESTION OF THE YEAR SORT OF DOES THAT TO ME..

PSST, FRANKLIN! I NEED TO BORROW A PENCIL AND SOME PAPER...

YOU HAD ALL SUMMER TO BUY THOSE THINGS... WHY ARE YOU JUST THINKING ABOUT THEM NOW?

9-5

TIRED OF PLAYING CENTER FIELD ON OUR TEAM, HUH, FRANKLIN?

QUICK, MARCIE, I NEED TO BORROW ANOTHER SHEET OF PAPER...

POLONIUS SAID, "NEITHER A BORROWER, NOR A LENDER BE"

9-6

POINT THAT KID OUT TO ME, AND I'LL TEACH HIM TO MIND HIS OWN BUSINESS!

"BORROWERS ARE NEARLY ALWAYS ILL-SPENDERS"

"WHO GOETH A BORROWING GOETH A SORROWING"

9-7

WHERE DO YOU GET THAT STUFF, MARCIE?

A BOOK OF QUOTATIONS..

COULD I BORROW IT?

MY FRIENDS SEEM TO THINK THAT I BORROW TOO MUCH, CHUCK..WHAT DO YOU THINK?

"A GOOD LATHER IS HALF THE SHAVE"

9-8

ARE YOU AWAKE, CHUCK?

"LLAMAS"

ONCE THERE WAS A MAN WHO OWNED TWO LLAMAS.

THEN HE GOT ANOTHER ONE. NOW HE HAD THREE LLLAMAS.

SOON HE HAD FOUR LLLLAMAS.

WHAT DID SHE GIVE YOU ON YOUR REPORT, SIR?

"DDDD-MINUS"

I ACTUALLY GOT A LETTER FROM PEGGY JEAN THIS MORNING..

SHE SAID SHE STILL THINKS ABOUT ME, AND STILL LIKES ME, AND..

STRIKE THREE!

9-13

WHAT HAPPENED TO STRIKE ONE AND STRIKE TWO?

YOU BLOCKHEAD! YOU STRUCK OUT, AND WE LOST THE LAST GAME OF THE SEASON!

9-14

YOU WERE STANDING THERE THINKING ABOUT YOUR NEW GIRLFRIEND, WEREN'T YOU?

I THOUGHT BEING IN LOVE WAS SUPPOSED TO MAKE YOU HAPPY..

WHERE'D YOU GET THAT IDEA?

9-15

THEN AGAIN, MAYBE THE ONLY REAL LOVE IS BETWEEN A BOY AND HIS DOG..

I COULD HAVE TOLD YOU THAT A LONG TIME AGO... ARE THERE ANY MORE COOKIES LEFT?

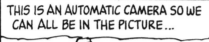

1990

PEANUTS
by SCHULZ

HERE'S THE FIERCE VULTURE WAITING HIGH IN A TREE FOR A VICTIM TO COME BY..

I HAVE A SUGGESTION FOR YOU..

I THINK YOU'RE FACING THE WRONG WAY...

I THINK YOU'LL FIND THAT MOST OF YOUR VICTIMS WILL BE COMING FROM THAT DIRECTION

10-7

I'M GOING TO HAVE TO LEARN NOT TO TAKE SUGGESTIONS..

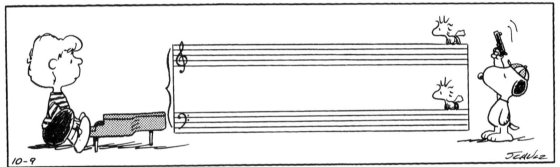

NO, THANK YOU..I'M NOT INTERESTED IN AWARDING THE WINNING TROPHY..

MUSICIANS PLAY A LOT OF LOVE SONGS, BUT THEY DON'T REALLY HEAR THEM, DO THEY?

ACTUALLY, THEY DON'T HEAR ANYTHING!

THIS NEXT PIECE IS A CONCERTO FOR FLUTE AND ORCHESTRA...

IT WAS COMPOSED BY ELLEN ZWILICH WHO, INCIDENTALLY, JUST HAPPENS TO BE A WOMAN!

GOOD GOING, ELLEN

1990

WHAT DID YOU LEARN IN SCHOOL TODAY?

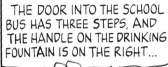

THE DOOR INTO THE SCHOOL BUS HAS THREE STEPS, AND THE HANDLE ON THE DRINKING FOUNTAIN IS ON THE RIGHT...

AND EVERYBODY TOLD ME THAT SECOND GRADE WAS GOING TO BE SO HARD!

ANOTHER ONE OF THOSE WHO DOESN'T TAKE THE GROCERY CART BACK..

GUESS WHAT I HAVE FOR LUNCH, MARCIE...THIRTY-FIVE FORTUNE COOKIES!

WHAT DOES THAT ONE SAY, SIR?

"WHO FIXES YOUR LUNCH, KID?"

I KNOW THE ANSWER!

BUT NOW I'VE FORGOTTEN IT..

HARD TO EXPLAIN HOW THE HUMAN MIND WORKS, HUH, MA'AM?

I GUESS IT'S GOING TO BE A NICE DAY AFTER ALL..

HERE, SNOOPY..THE SCHOOL BUS IS COMING..WHY DON'T YOU TAKE MY CAP AND UMBRELLA HOME FOR ME?

BUT YOU DON'T HAVE TO MAKE A BIG DEAL OUT OF IT!

HERE..YOUR COLLAR JUST CAME BACK FROM THE CLEANERS

I'M GLAD TO SEE THAT YOU TAKE SUCH GOOD CARE OF YOUR THINGS..

11-15

BUT WHAT AM I GOING TO DO WITH ALL THE HANGERS?

YES, MA'AM...WELL, SINCE SCHOOL STARTED, MY DOG HAS BEEN VERY UPSET...

BECAUSE I'M NOT HOME, HE'S HAD TO FORGO HIS MID-MORNING SNACK, HIS NOON SNACK AND HIS MID-AFTERNOON SNACK...YES, MA'AM, I SEE...

11-16

I SHOULD HAVE WARNED YOU.. MISS OTHMAR IS A STRONG BELIEVER IN FORGOING..

IT'S BEEN A LONG TIME SINCE I'VE SEEN A REAL STOCKING CAP..

11-17

HE SCORES!

THAT WAS A GOOD GAME!

IN MY DOGHOUSE?

11-18

WELL, I SUPPOSE IT WOULD BE ALL RIGHT..

I GUESS THEY HAVE TO HAVE SOMEPLACE TO PARK THE ZAMBONI..

WHAT IF I DECIDED TO BECOME A WAITER SOMEDAY?

I'VE HAD A LOT OF EXPERIENCE FEEDING MY DOG...

PROBABLY, HOWEVER, NOT THE SORT OF THING TO PUT ON A RÉSUMÉ..

11-19

ALL RIGHT, YOU STUPID BEAGLE, LET GO OF THIS BLANKET RIGHT NOW!

11-20

I SAID, "RIGHT NOW!"

I NEVER KNOW IF "RIGHT NOW" MEANS "RIGHT NOW" OR "RIGHT NOW"...

Dear

WHAT WAS HIS NAME AGAIN?

WHO?

THE FAT GUY WITH THE WHITE BEARD AND THE RED SUIT...

11-21

WHY ARE YOU WRITING TO MY SUBSTITUTE MATH TEACHER?

HAPPY THANKSGIVING, OL' PAL!

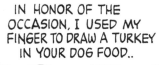

IN HONOR OF THE OCCASION, I USED MY FINGER TO DRAW A TURKEY IN YOUR DOG FOOD..

I DARE YOU TO LICK IT OFF!

11-22

Dear Santa Claus, I demand that you bring me the following items this year.

THAT'S PRETTY STRONG LANGUAGE, ISN'T IT?

Please.

11-23

HERE..YOUR LETTER CAME BACK MARKED "INSUFFICIENT ADDRESS"

"INSUFFICIENT"?! LOOK WHAT I WROTE...

"SANTA CLAUS.. NORTH POLE.. WHEREVER THAT IS.. ZIP CODE.. WHO KNOWS? PLEASE FORWARD.. WHY NOT?"

MAYBE YOU SHOULD UNDERLINE ALL THE WORDS AND PUT IN SOME HYPHENS..

11-24

1990

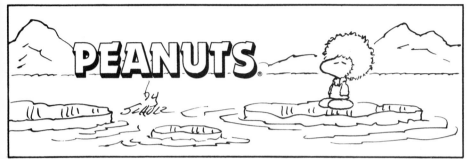

LUCY SAID IF I NEED TWENTY-FIVE DOLLARS TO BUY PEGGY JEAN A CHRISTMAS PRESENT, I SHOULD SELL MY DOG...

WHAT A GREAT IDEA!

THAT'S THE FIRST TIME I'VE EVER SEEN HIM SPILL HIS WATER DISH..

12/6

YOU DON'T HAVE TO WORRY, SNOOPY...I'D NEVER SELL YOU.. YOU AND I ARE FRIENDS... WE'RE BUDDIES..IN FACT, YOU'RE THE BEST THING THAT'S EVER HAPPENED TO ME...

I KNOW

12-7

YES, MA'AM ... I'M LOOKING AT THOSE GLOVES AGAIN...

I WISH I COULD GET THEM FOR THIS GIRL I KNOW, BUT I CAN'T AFFORD THEM..

12-8

I JUST LIKE TO STAND HERE, AND PRETEND I'M BUYING THEM FOR HER..

SORRY, MA'AM, I DIDN'T REALIZE I WAS FOGGING UP THE GLASS..

12-10

GO AHEAD, ASK HIM..

IS THIS THE BUS STOP?

-FOR SALE-
JOE GARAGIOLA
AUTOGRAPHED BASEBALL

MAKE ME AN OFFER

ALL I HAVE IS A DIME.. WILL I GET CHANGE?

DO YOU HAVE A BILLIE JEAN KING?

12-11

-FOR SALE-
USED COMIC BOOKS

ARE THESE ALL YOU HAVE?

YES, MA'AM.. I SOLD MY WHOLE COLLECTION OF COMIC BOOKS..SEE? HERE'S THE MONEY! NOW, I CAN BUY THOSE GLOVES FOR THAT GIRL I LIKE...

12-12

BROWNIE CHARLES!

PEGGY JEAN! WHAT ARE YOU DOING HERE?

I'VE BEEN SHOPPING WITH MY MOTHER..LOOK, I JUST BOUGHT THIS NEW PAIR OF GLOVES!

1990

I REMEMBER WHEN I WAS SMALL AND I LIVED AT THE DAISY HILL PUPPY FARM, WE ALWAYS HAD A CHRISTMAS TREE...

12-20

AND IT ALWAYS HAD A LITTLE STAR ON THE TOP..

THAT WAS A LONG TIME AGO..

ONE OF THE GREAT JOYS OF LIFE IS SITTING BY YOUR CHRISTMAS TREE WHILE BIG FLUFFY SNOWFLAKES FLOAT GENTLY TO THE GROUND...

12-21

OR A NICE SANDSTORM

SANDSTORMS ARE DIFFERENT FROM SNOWSTORMS...

AFTER A SNOWSTORM, WE USED TO RUN OUTSIDE AND BUILD A SNOWMAN..WE'D USE A CARROT FOR HIS NOSE...

RIGHT NOW, IF I HAD A CARROT, I'D EAT IT!

12-22

PEANUTS® by SCHULZ

WHAT ARE YOU DOING?

I'M LEAVING A PLATE OF COOKIES UNDER OUR TREE FOR SANTA CLAUS

AND IF I HIDE SOMEPLACE, MAYBE I'LL EVEN GET TO SEE HIM...

IT WORKED! I SAW HIM!! I SAW SANTA CLAUS!

12-23

BUT I NEVER REALIZED HE WAS SO SHORT..

MARCIE, WHAT BOOK WERE WE SUPPOSED TO READ DURING THANKSGIVING VACATION?

12-27

THIS IS CHRISTMAS VACATION, SIR..

CHRISTMAS VACATION?! HOW CAN I READ SOMETHING DURING CHRISTMAS VACATION WHEN I DIDN'T READ WHAT I WAS SUPPOSED TO READ DURING THANKSGIVING VACATION?

DUCK, SIR! EASTER IS COMING!!

LET ME KNOW WHEN MY TOAST POPS UP...

12-28

ALREADY? THANK YOU..

I'VE NEVER SEEN ANYBODY SO COMPLETELY USELESS!

HAVE YOU ANY IDEA WHAT YOU'RE GOING TO DO WITH THE REST OF YOUR LIFE?

I'VE BEEN THINKING OF GIVING SLEEPING LESSONS..

12-29

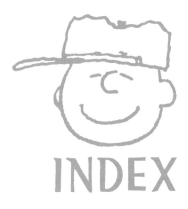

INDEX

Alistair Beagle (Snoopy as...)... 77

"Anna Karenina"... 283

Audobon Special... 96

Autumn... 275, 276

Baby Aspirin... 177

Badminton... 150, 161

Baseball... 21, 31, 32, 33, 35, 36, 38, 39, 41, 42, 45, 47, 48, 53, 57, 63, 79, 80, 81, 84, 85, 86, 100, 102, 103, 113, 175. 176, 185, 186, 190, 191, 195, 196, 202, 214, 216, 239, 240, 254, 255, 258, 266, 305

Basketball... 215

Beach... 235

Beachball... 269, 270

Beagle Scouts... 52, 76, 101, 102, 128, 256, 269, 270, 271, 307

Bean bags... 4, 5, 17, 28, 54, 66, 77, 83, 156, 168, 173, 180, 215, 219, 230, 233, 266, 269, 288, 290, 296, 300, 303, 306

Bean ball... 39, 41, 42

Bear... 174

Bible, the ... 306

Bible quiz... 28

Bible verses... 28

Birdbath... 110, 111, 116

Blankets... 26, 43, 50, 51, 81, 159, 163, 215, 225, 227, 234, 236, 275, 296, 313

Bones... 152

Books... 95, 191, 234, 311

Brown, Charlie... 2, 3, 4, 5, 8, 10, 13, 15, 16, 17, 18, 20, 21, 22, 24, 25, 26, 29, 30, 31, 32, 33, 34, 35, 36, 37, 39, 40, 41, 42, 45, 47, 48, 49, 53, 54, 57, 60, 61, 62, 63, 64, 66, 67, 68, 69, 71, 72, 73, 74, 75, 77, 78, 79, 80, 81, 82, 83, 84, 85, 86, 87, 89, 90, 91, 92, 93, 94, 95, 96, 97, 98, 100, 101, 102, 103, 104, 107, 112, 113, 116, 117, 118, 125, 126, 128, 129, 131, 132, 134, 135, 136, 137, 138, 140, 142, 144, 146, 150, 155, 156, 157, 158, 164, 166, 167, 168, 169, 170, 172, 173, 175, 177, 178, 179, 180, 181, 184, 185, 186, 188, 189, 190, 191, 193, 194, 195, 196, 199, 201, 202, 207, 209, 210. 211, 212, 213, 214, 215, 216, 218, 219, 220, 224, 225, 229, 230, 231, 232, 233, 234, 237, 239, 240, 241, 242, 243, 246, 248, 249, 251, 252, 254, 255, 257, 258, 260, 264, 266, 267, 272, 273, 276, 280, 281, 282, 284, 285, 286, 287, 290, 291, 293, 294, 296, 297, 299, 300, 302, 303, 304, 305, 306, 307, 308, 310, 311, 312

Brown, Sally... 2, 4, 5, 10, 13, 23, 29, 30, 34, 49, 54, 56, 60, 66, 68, 77, 80, 81, 83, 84, 87, 89, 93, 94, 96, 97, 101, 104, 107, 112, 116, 117, 125, 126, 131, 132, 134, 136, 138, 140, 142, 146, 150, 151, 153, 155, 156, 158, 161, 168, 173, 174, 177, 186, 191, 200, 201, 212, 213, 215, 218, 219, 229, 230, 239, 241, 254, 257, 258, 260, 266, 269, 272, 273, 276, 282, 284, 285, 287, 288, 290, 291, 296, 297, 300, 303, 304, 306, 308, 310, 311

Bugs... 162

Bus Stop... 23, 107, 138, 140, 146, 204, 217, 287, 291, 293

Cactus... 27, 60, 99, 141, 188, 189, 222, 233, 254, 309, 311, 314

Camera... 273

Camp... 68, 69, 71, 72, 74, 197, 198, 218, 219, 242, 243, 244, 245, 246, 248, 249, 251, 252, 302

Camping... 101, 198, 244, 270, 307

Candy... 70, 272

Canoeing... 110, 111, 116, 219, 242, 243

Cards... 150, 154, 229

"Casablanca"... 106

Charlie Brown's Grampa... 24, 83

Chicken Pox... 121

Chisholm Trail... 272

Chocolate chip cookies... 225

Christmas... 154, 155, 173, 257, 300, 302, 303, 309, 310, 312

Christmas Eve... 311

"Citizen Kane"... 93, 206

Cloud... 199

Coconut... 12

Comic books... 305, 306

Concert... 64, 77, 279, 298

Cookies... 12, 18, 85, 86, 124, 127, 129, 134, 136, 158, 164, 170, 178, 185, 201, 206, 209, 210, 218, 225, 242, 243, 245, 257, 261, 267, 281, 285, 290, 310

Comb... 182

Concert... 64, 66, 70

Croquet... 102

Crown.... 203

"D-minus"... 17, 68, 69, 111, 117, 146, 228, 265

Dancing... 25

DiMaggio, Joe... 98

Dinosaurs... 243

Doughnuts... 53, 59, 119, 162

Dwyer, Richard... 181

Easter... 312

Father's Day... 73

Field trip... 200, 201

Fishing... 238

Fish Tank... 284
Fleming, Peggy... 181
Football... 113, 114, 118, 133, 148, 248, 249, 251, 280, 291
Fort Zinderneuf... 269
Franklin... 18, 81, 98, 113, 116, 152, 177, 189, 201, 239, 254, 263, 294, 311
Garagiola, Joe... 240, 305
Garvey, Steve... 98
Golf... 15, 29, 61, 78, 83, 86, 91, 106, 146, 180, 188, 189, 207, 213, 230, 251, 299
Grand Canyon... 225
"The Great Gatsby"... 244
Great Pumpkin... 121, 124, 127, 130, 286
Hiking... 197, 198, 219,
Hockey... 14, 144, 174, 295,
Hot chocolate... 155
Hot dog... 243
Howe, Gene...229
Ice.. 181
Ice cream... 18, 83, 92, 93
Ice show... 98
Ice skating... 7, 13
Igloo... 301
"Ivanhoe"... 281
Jackson, Michael... 240
Jury duty... 209, 210
King of the Jungle... 203, 204
Kipling, Rudyard... 129
Kites... 34, 184
"Laurel and Hardy"... 292
Leaves... 275
Liberty head dime... 220
Library... 93, 224
Life jacket... 242, 243
Little Red-Haired Girl... 20, 21, 25, 67, 82, 167

Llamas... 265
Lunch... 19, 25, 138, 162, 290
Lydia... 159, 176, 192, 218

Marcie... 2, 5, 14, 19, 26, 27, 38, 39, 40, 41, 42, 48, 59, 64, 66, 68, 69, 70, 71, 72, 74, 75, 77, 95, 96, 98, 101, 107, 110, 111, 113, 114, 119, 120, 132, 133, 137, 138, 139, 143, 146, 147, 148, 149, 157, 162, 165, 171, 176, 180, 182, 187, 188, 192, 195, 200, 208, 217, 221, 222, 224, 226, 227, 228, 231, 233, 241, 263, 264, 265, 279, 280, 281, 282, 283, 284, 285, 290, 291, 292, 298, 312
Marshmallows... 101, 102, 155, 198
Masked Marvel (Lucy as) ... 35
Mickey Mouse... 237
Mississippi River... 221
Molly Volley... 268
Moon... 191, 213
Movie theater... 179, 239, 241
National Endowment for the Arts... 222, 224
Napoleon... 221
New Year's... 156

New Year's Day... 158
Newspaper... 289
Obedience School... 151
October Beast (Snoopy as)... 275
Olaf... 8, 9, 11, 12, 58
Opera...166
Othmar, Miss... 294
Patty... 273
Pancakes... 22
Paperback... 213
Peggy Jean... 245, 246, 248, 249, 251, 252, 253, 258, 260, 266, 267, 300, 302, 303, 305
Peppermint Patty... 2, 5, 14, 17, 19, 24, 26, 27, 39, 40, 41, 42, 48, 53, 59, 62, 63, 64, 65, 66, 68, 69, 70, 71, 72, 74, 75, 77, 93, 95, 96, 98, 101, 107, 110, 111, 113, 114, 115, 117, 119, 132, 133, 135, 137, 138, 139, 143, 146, 148, 157, 161, 164, 165, 168, 171, 176, 180, 182, 187, 188, 192, 193, 195, 208, 217, 221, 222, 224, 226, 227, 228, 231, 233, 263, 264, 265, 279, 280, 282, 283, 285, 290, 291, 292, 293, 298, 312
Pigpen... 29, 30, 31, 272, 272
Pitcher's Mound... 1, 21, 32, 33, 35, 36, 38, 39, 41, 45, 47, 53, 63, 79, 80, 81, 86, 102, 103, 196, 266
Pizza... 291, 307
"Ploughman's lunch"... 243
Polar Bear (Snoopy as...)... 3
Present.... 154, 155, 173
Psychiatric help... 29, 30, 128, 169, 199
Radio... 150

Rain... 186, 200, 201, 203, 207, 232, 257
Red Baron, The... 120
Rollerskating... 291
Root beer... 86, 119, 135, 149
Sand castle... 235
Sandstorm... 309
Santa Claus... 152, 153, 154, 296, 297, 299, 308, 310, 311
Scarecrow... 223
Scarf... 149
School... 2, 17, 19, 24, 26, 27, 32, 35, 36, 44, 48, 53, 59, 67, 69, 82, 107, 110, 115, 117, 119, 125, 129, 131, 132, 135, 137, 138, 139, 140, 143, 146, 165, 167, 168, 176, 180, 182, 191, 192, 201, 208, 220, 221, 226, 227, 231, 263, 264, 265, 265, 272, 283, 285, 292, 293, 294
School bus... 158, 161, 162, 164, 165, 179, 200, 287, 290
Schroeder... 32, 47, 105, 122, 123, 179, 182, 186, 192, 201, 206, 207, 214, 216, 228, 232, 240, 247, 258, 206, 278, 279, 293
Sheep... 165
Shepherd... 165
Shlabotnik, Joe... 98
Shoeless Joe Beagle (Snoopy as...)... 103
Shovel... 161
Sledding... 17, 151
Snoopy... 2, 5, 6, 7, 8, 9, 10, 11, 12, 13, 14, 15, 16, 18, 20, 21, 22, 24, 26, 29, 31, 36, 37, 43, 45, 46, 47, 49, 50, 51, 52, 53, 54, 55, 56, 57, 58, 59, 60, 61,

62, 65, 69, 71, 72, 73, 74, 75, 76, 77, 78, 79, 80, 81, 84, 85, 86, 88, 89, 90, 91, 92, 93, 94, 96, 97, 98, 99, 100, 101, 102, 103, 104, 105, 106, 108, 109, 110, 111, 113, 114, 116, 117, 119, 120, 122, 123, 124, 125, 126, 127, 128, 129, 130, 131, 132, 134, 135, 137, 140, 142, 144, 146, 147, 149, 150, 151, 152, 153, 154, 155, 156, 158, 159, 160, 162, 164, 165, 167, 168, 170, 171, 172, 174, 176, 178, 179, 180, 181, 182, 183, 186, 188, 189, 191, 192, 194, 195, 197, 198, 201, 202, 203, 204, 205, 206, 207, 209, 210, 211, 212, 213, 216, 218, 219, 221, 223, 224, 225, 227, 228, 229, 230, 234, 235, 236, 237, 238, 239, 240, 241, 242, 243, 244, 245, 247, 248, 249, 250, 251, 252, 253, 255, 256, 257, 259, 260, 261, 267, 268, 269, 270, 271, 273, 274, 275, 276, 277, 278, 279, 280, 281, 282, 284, 285, 287, 288, 289, 290, 293, 294, 295, 296, 297, 299, 301, 302, 303, 306, 307, 310, 311, 312, 313

Snoopy's dad... 36, 58, 73
Snoopy's mom... 58
Snow... 1, 3, 144, 145, 151, 158, 159, 161, 163, 164, 172, 175, 276, 295, 301, 308
Snowman... 143, 158, 172, 175, 309
Soccer... 219
Spike... 5, 6, 27, 58, 60, 99, 141,

222, 224, 233, 309, 314
Stevens, Wallace...220
Stocking Cap... 294
Stonehenge... 161
Summer reading... 95, 96
Summer school... 68, 69, 71, 227, 228, 231, 233
Sundae... 198, 227
Sweatshirt... 148
Symphony... 14
Telephone... 157, 174, 182, 219, 224, 228, 231, 233, 245, 246, 248, 249, 251, 252, 263, 264, 281, 282, 284
Television... 17, 93, 28, 56, 155, 156, 164, 180, 210, 212, 217, 219, 230, 241, 269, 288, 306
Tennis... 219, 253, 255, 268
Thanksgiving... 156, 297, 312
Throne... 204, 235
Toast... 312
Tolstoy, Leo... 283
Traffic signals... 150, 218
Trees... 170, 184, 189, 193, 201, 227, 275, 277
Tug-of-war... 234
Turkey... 297
Typewriter... 2, 5, 6, 8, 55, 56, 109, 137, 183, 206, 261
Ugly Dog Contest... 5 - 6, 8, 9, 11, 12
Valentine's Day... 20, 21, 176
Van Pelt, Linus... 1, 5, 17, 21, 23, 24, 25, 26, 28, 31, 32, 33, 35, 38, 43, 48, 49, 50, 51, 59, 65, 67, 80, 81, 82, 83, 98, 99, 100, 101, 102, 103, 104, 105, 107, 108, 117, 121, 124, 125, 126, 127, 129, 130, 131, 135,

137, 143, 145, 146, 150, 152, 156, 159, 161, 162, 163, 164, 165, 166, 168, 170, 176, 179, 185, 192, 194, 200, 201, 206, 215, 216, 218, 225, 227, 234, 235, 236, 237, 239, 241, 245, 246, 248, 249, 251, 252, 254, 258, 261, 262, 273, 275, 277, 286, 287, 294, 296, 299, 302, 306, 308, 313

Van Pelt, Lucy... 1, 3, 5, 6, 7, 8, 9, 11, 13, 15, 28, 29, 30, 31, 33, 35, 36, 38, 45, 47, 48, 49, 50, 51, 53, 55, 57, 63, 80, 81, 83, 98, 99, 100, 101, 102, 104, 105, 108, 118, 123, 128, 137, 145, 152, 155, 156, 159, 163, 164, 165, 168, 169, 179, 181, 183, 190, 192, 195, 196, 199, 201, 206, 228, 207, 214, 216, 223, 232, 235, 237, 239, 240, 241, 248, 252, 254, 255, 256, 261, 262, 266, 267, 267, 272, 273, 299, 302, 306, 308, 311, 312
Veterans Day... 135
Violet... 5, 81, 168, 201, 241, 273

Volcanoes... 215, 226
Vulture, the (Snoopy as...)... 277
Watchdog... 18
Western paintings... 222, 225
Williams, Ted... 98
Wills, Maury... 98
Wimbledon... 228
Wind... 182, 184
Woodstock... 3, 14, 24, 29, 36, 37, 46, 52, 54, 61, 76, 78, 88, 91, 96, 100, 101, 102, 106, 110, 111, 114, 116, 120, 128, 143, 144, 152, 153, 154, 160, 161, 165, 167, 176, 189, 192, 194, 197, 198, 203, 204, 221, 230, 238, 269, 276, 278, 279, 287, 288, 290, 295, 299, 301, 307
Woodstock's friends (Bill, Conrad, Harriet, Olivier and Raymond, Wilson)... 37, 52, 54, 61, 76, 91, 96, 100, 101, 102, 114, 144, 150, 153, 159, 171, 174, 179, 192, 194, 197, 198, 244, 269, 270, 271, 278, 279, 287, 295, 307
World Famous Attorney... 23, 38, 65, 80, 125, 126, 261
World Famous Sergeant-Major of the Foreign Legion... 61, 269, 270, 271
World Famous Surgeon... 104, 105, 108
World War I... 210
World War I Flying Ace... 14, 69, 71, 72, 74, 75, 119, 120, 135, 147, 149
Zamboni... 3, 98, 295

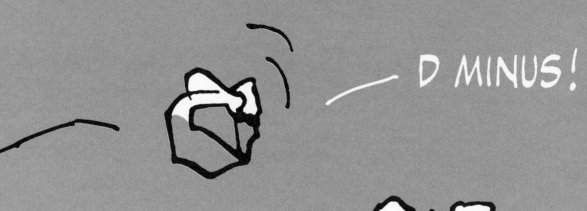

CHARLES M. SCHULZ · 1922 to 2000

Charles M. Schulz was born November 26, 1922 in Minneapolis. His destiny was foreshadowed when an uncle gave him, at the age of two days, the nickname Sparky (after the racehorse Spark Plug in the newspaper strip *Barney Google*).

Schulz grew up in St. Paul. By all accounts, he led an unremarkable, albeit sheltered, childhood. He was an only child, close to both parents, his eventual career path nurtured by his father, who bought four Sunday papers every week — just for the comics.

An outstanding student, he skipped two grades early on, but began to flounder in high school — perhaps not so coincidentally at the same time kids are going through their cruelest, most status-conscious period of socialization. The pain, bitterness, insecurity, and failures chronicled in *Peanuts* appear to have originated from this period of Schulz's life.

Although Schulz enjoyed sports, he also found refuge in solitary activities: reading, drawing, and watching movies. He bought comic books and Big Little Books, pored over the newspaper strips, and copied his favorites — *Buck Rogers*, the Walt Disney characters, *Popeye, Tim Tyler's Luck*. He quickly became a connoisseur; his heroes were Milton Caniff, Roy Crane, Hal Foster, and Alex Raymond.

In his senior year in high school, his mother noticed an ad in a local newspaper for a correspondence school, Federal Schools (later called Art

Instruction Schools). Schulz passed the talent test, completed the course and began trying, unsuccessfully, to sell gag cartoons to magazines. (His first published drawing was of his dog, Spike, and appeared in a 1937 *Ripley's Believe It Or Not!* installment.)

After World War II had ended and Schulz was discharged from the army, he started submitting gag cartoons to the various magazines of the time; his first breakthrough, however, came when an editor at *Timeless Topix* hired him to letter adventure comics. Soon after that, he was hired by his alma mater, Art Instruction, to correct student lessons returned by mail.

Between 1948 and 1950, he succeeded in selling 17 cartoons to the *Saturday Evening Post* — as well as, to the local *St. Paul Pioneer Press*, a weekly comic feature called *Li'l Folks*. It was run in the women's section and paid $10 a week. After writing and drawing the feature for two years, Schulz asked for a better location in the paper or for daily exposure, as well as a raise. When he was turned down on all three counts, he quit.

He started submitting strips to the newspaper syndicates. In the Spring of 1950, he received a letter from the United Feature Syndicate, announcing their interest in his submission, *Li'l Folks*. Schulz boarded a train in June for New York City; more interested in doing a strip than a panel, he also brought along the first installments

of what would become *Peanuts* — and that was what sold. (The title, which Schulz loathed to his dying day, was imposed by the syndicate). The first *Peanuts* daily appeared October 2, 1950; the first Sunday, January 6, 1952.

Prior to *Peanuts*, the province of the comics page had been that of gags, social and political observation, domestic comedy, soap opera, and various adventure genres. Although *Peanuts* changed, or evolved, during the 50 years Schulz wrote and drew it, it remained, as it began, an anomaly on the comics page — a comic strip about the interior crises of the cartoonist himself. After a painful divorce in 1973 from which he had not yet recovered, Schulz told a reporter, "Strangely, I've drawn better cartoons in the last six months — or as good as I've ever drawn. I don't know how the human mind works." Surely, it was this kind of humility in the face of profoundly irreducible human question that makes *Peanuts* as universally moving as it is.

Diagnosed with cancer, Schulz retired from *Peanuts* at the end of 1999. He died on February 12th 2000, the day before his last strip was published (and two days before Valentine's Day) — having completed 17,897 daily and Sunday strips, each and every one fully written, drawn, and lettered entirely by his own hand — an unmatched achievement in comics.

—*Gary Groth*

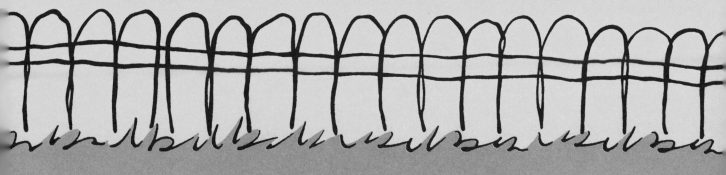

Also available from Canongate *The Complete Peanuts: 1987-1988*

In this latest collection, romance is in the air. Charlie Brown's attempt at flirting in class sends him to the school nurse, while Linus is thwarted in his attempt to woo 'Lydia' of the many names. Other storylines include Snoopy's sojourn in the hospital for a hockey-related knee injury, Sally's bumpy career as a playwright, and Snoopy's 'kiss-and-tell' book. Plus Rerun, Spike, Peppermint Patty and Marcie . . . and Snoopy's feathered Beagle Scouts.